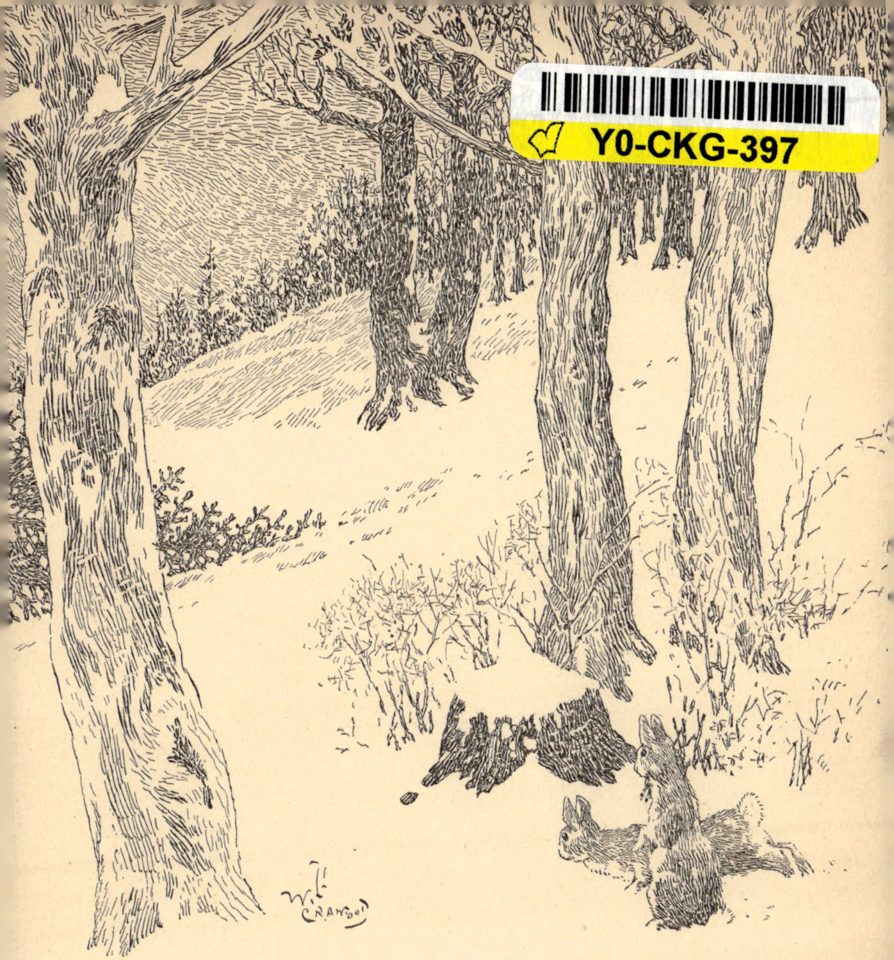

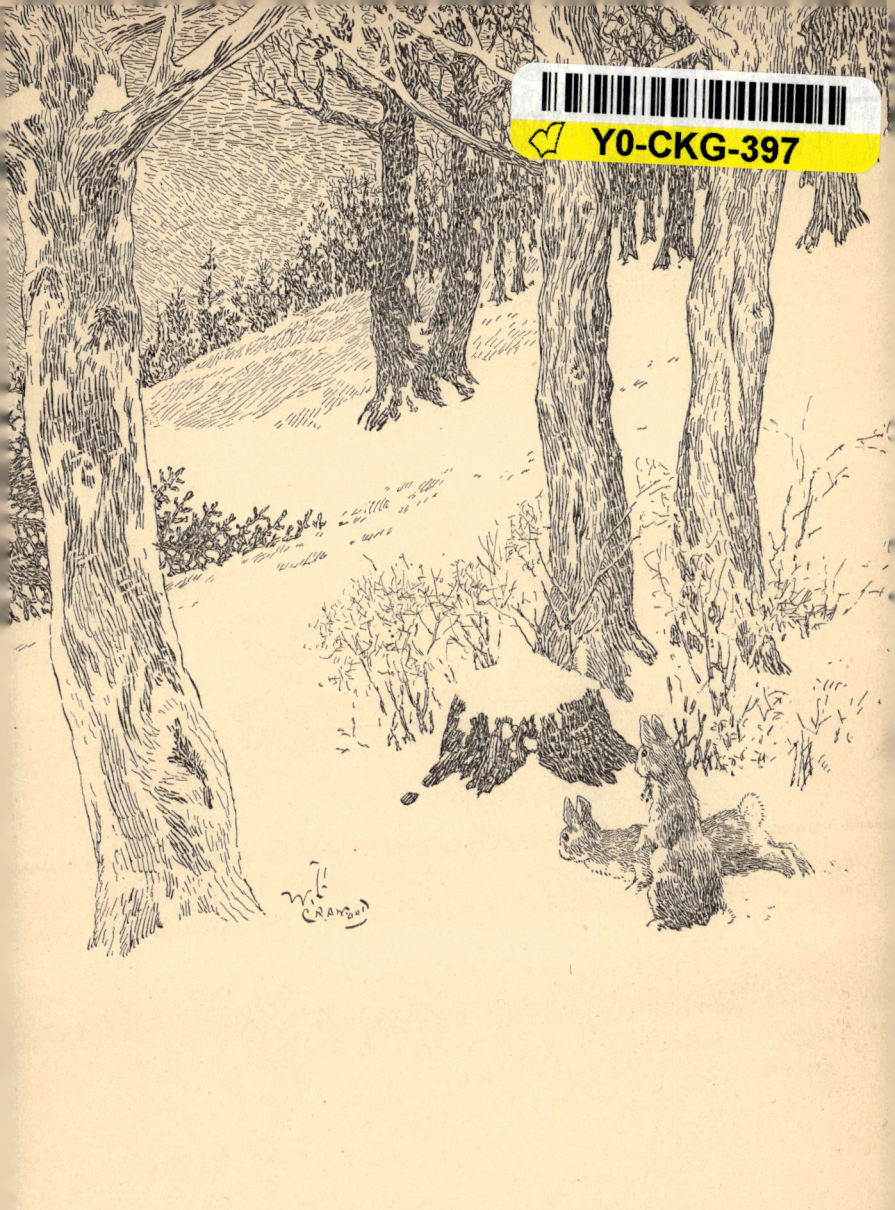

By Cyrus Townsend Brady

And Thus He Came

The More Excellent Way

A Little Book for Christmas

The author making his book, as pictured by his friend,
Will Crawford.

A Little Book for Christmas

Containing a Greeting, a Word of Advice, Some Personal Adventures, a Carol, a Meditation, and Three Christmas Stories for All Ages

By

Cyrus Townsend Brady

Author of
"And Thus He Came, A Christmas Fantasy," "Christmas When the West Was Young," etc., etc.

With Illustrations and Decorations by
Will Crawford

G. P. Putnam's Sons
New York and London
The Knickerbocker Press
1917

COPYRIGHT, 1917, BY
CYRUS TOWNSEND BRADY

The Knickerbocker Press, New York

Dedicated

TO

MRS. LEONARD L. HILL

AND HER CHARMING COMPANIONS

OF

THE AMERICAN CRITERION SOCIETY

OF NEW YORK

BY

THEIR CHAPLAIN

Preface

CHRISTMAS is one of the great days of obligation and observance in the Church of which I am a Priest; but it is much more than that, it is one of the great days of obligation and observance in the world. Furthermore it is one of the evidences of the power of Him Whose birth we commemorate that its observation is not limited by conditions of race and creed. Those who fail to see in Him what we see nevertheless see something and even by imperfect visions are moved to joy. The world transmutes that joy into blessing, not merely by giving of its substance but of its soul because men perceive that it is for the soul's good and because they hope to receive its benefits although they well know that giving is far better than receiving, in the very words of Him Who gave us the greatest of all gifts—Himself.

As a Priest of the Church, as a Missionary in the Far West, as the Rector of large and important parishes I have been brought in touch with varied life. Christmas in all its phases is familiar to me. The author of many books and stories as well as the preacher of many sermons, it is natural that Christmas should have engaged a large part of my attention. Out of the abundance of material which I have accumulated in the course of a long ministry and a longer life I have gathered here a sheaf of things I have written about Christmas; personal adventures, stories suggested by the old yet ever-new theme; meditations, words of advice which I am old enough to be entitled to give; and last but not least good wishes and good will. I might even call this little volume *A Book of Good Will toward Men*. And so fit it not only for Christmas but for all other seasons as well.

If it shall add to your joy in Christmas, dear reader, and better still, if it shall move you to add to the joy of some one else at Christmas-tide or in any other season, I shall be well repaid for my efforts and incidentally you will also be repaid for your purchase.

CYRUS TOWNSEND BRADY.

THE HEMLOCKS, PARK HILL,
   YONKERS, N. Y.
     1917

Note of Acknowledgement

The author is in debt to his long-time and greatly beloved friend the Rev. Alsop Leffingwell for the beautiful musical setting of the little carol which this book contains.

TABLE OF CONTENTS

		PAGE
I.—A CHRISTMAS GREETING	. .	1

"*Peace on Earth, Good Will toward Men*"

II.—FROM A FAR COUNTRY . . 13

A story for grown-ups
Being a new variation of an ancient theme

III.—ON CHRISTMAS GIVING . . 59

Being a word of much needed advice

IV.—IT WAS THE SAME CHRISTMAS MORNING 69

A story for girls
In which it is shown how different the same thing may be

V.—A CHRISTMAS CAROL . . . 81

To be sung to the music accompanying it

VI.—THE LONE SCOUT'S CHRISTMAS . 85

A story for boys
Wherein is set forth the courage of youth

Contents

		PAGE
VII.—Looking into the Manger	115
A Christmas meditation	
VIII.—Christmas in the Snows	141
Being some personal adventures in the Far West	
IX.—A Christmas Wish	173
For everybody everywhere	

Illustrations

	PAGE
THE AUTHOR MAKING HIS BOOK *Frontispiece*	
"I SOUGHT DAT SANTY CLAUS TAME DOWN DE CHIMNEY," SAID THE YOUNGER OF THE TWAIN	46
"I AM SURE, MISS, THAT THEY DO WISH YOU A MERRY CHRISTMAS"	76
"THE STARS LOOK DOWN"	84
"THRUSTING HIS TOES INTO THE STRAPS HE STRUCK OUT BOLDLY"	96
"THE WORLD BOWS DOWN TO A MOTHER AND HER CHILD—AND THE MOTHER HERSELF IS AT THE FEET OF THE CHILD"	124

A Christmas Greeting

A CHRISTMAS GREETING

"Good Will Toward Men"—St. Luke 11-14.

THERE was a time when the spirit of Christmas was of the present. There is a period when most of it is of the past. There shall come a day perhaps when all of it will be of the future. The child time, the present; the middle years, the past; old age, the future.

Come to my mind Christmas Days of long ago. As a boy again I enter into the spirit of the Christmas stockings hanging before my fire. I know what the children think to-day. I recall what they feel.

Passes childhood, and I look down the nearer years. There rise before me remembrances of Christmas Days on storm-tossed seas, where waves beat upon the ice-bound ship. I recall again the bitter touch of water-warping winter, of drifts of snow, of wind-swept plains. In the gamut of my remembrance I am once more in the poor, mean, lonely little sanctuary out on the prairie, with a handful of Christians, mostly women, gathered together in the freezing, draughty building. In later years I worship in the great cathedral church, ablaze with lights, verdant and fragrant with the evergreen pines, echoing with joyful carols and celestial harmonies. My recollections are of contrasts like those of life—joy and sadness, poverty and ease.

And the pictures are full of faces, many of which may be seen no more by earthly vision. I miss the clasp of vanished hands,

I crave the sound of voices stilled. As we old and older grow, there is a note of sadness in our glee. Whether we will or not we must twine the cypress with the holly. The recollection of each passing year brings deeper regret. How many have gone from those circles that we recall when we were children? How many little feet that pattered upon the stair on Christmas morning now tread softer paths and walk in broader ways; sisters and brothers who used to come back from the far countries to the old home—alas, they cannot come from the farther country in which they now are, and perhaps, saddest thought of all, we would not wish them to come again. How many, with whom we joined hands around the Christmas tree, have gone?

Circles are broken, families are separated, loved ones are lost, but the old world sweeps on. Others come to take our places. As we stood at the knee of some unforgotten mother, so other children stand. As we listened to the story of the Christ Child from the lips of some grey old father, so other children listen and we ourselves perchance are fathers or mothers too. Other groups come to us for the deathless story. Little heads which recall vanished halcyon days of youth bend around another younger mother. Smaller hands than ours write letters to Santa Claus and hear the story, the sweetest story ever told, of the Baby who came to Mary and through her to all the daughters and sons of women on that winter night on the Bethlehem hills.

And we thank God for the children who take us out of the past, out of ourselves, away from recollections that weigh us down; the children that weave in the woof and warp of life when our own youth has passed, some of the buoyancy, the joy, the happiness of the present; the children in whose opening lives we turn hopefully to the future. We thank God at this Christmas season that it pleased Him to send His beloved Son to come to us as a little child, like any other child. We thank God that in the lesser sense we may see in every child who comes to-day another incarnation of divinity. We thank God for the portion of His Spirit with which He dowers every child of man, just as we thank Him for pouring it all upon the Infant in the Manger.

There is no age that has not had its prophet. No country, no people, but that has produced its leader. But did any of them ever before come as a little child? Did any of them begin to lead while yet in arms? Lodges there upon any other baby brow "the round and top of sovereignty?" What distinguished Christ and His Christian followers from all the world? Behold! no mighty monarch, but "a little child shall lead them!"

You may see through the glass darkly, you may not know or understand the blessedness of faith in Him as He would have you know it, but there is nothing that can dim the light that radiates from that birth in the rude cave back of the inn. Ah, it pierces through the darkness of that shrouding night. It shines to-day. Still sparkles the Star in the East. He is that Star.

There is nothing that can take from mankind—even doubting mankind—the spirit of Christ and the Christmas season. Our celebrations do not rest upon the conclusions of logic, or the demonstrations of philosophy; I would not even argue that they depend inevitably or absolutely upon the possession of a certain faith in Jesus, but we accept Christmas, nevertheless; we endeavour to apply the Christmas spirit, for just once in the year; it may be because we cannot, try as we may, crush out utterly and entirely the divinity that is in us that makes for God. The stories and tales for Christmas which have for their theme the hard heart softened are not mere fictions of the imagination. They rest upon an instinctive consciousness of a profound philosophic truth.

What is the unpardonable sin, I wonder? Is it to be persistently and forever unkind? Does it mean perhaps the absolute refusal to accept the principle of love which is indeed creation's final law? The lessons of the Christmastide are so many; the appeals that now may be made to humanity crowd to the lips from full minds and fuller hearts. Might we not reduce them all to the explication of the underlying principle of God's purpose to us, as expressed in those themic words of love with which angels and men greeted the advent of the Child on the first Christmas morning, "Good will toward men?"

Let us then show our good will toward

men by doing good and bringing happiness to someone—if not to everyone—at this Christmas season. Put aside the memories of disappointments, of sorrows that have not vanished, of cares that still burden, and do good in spite of them because you would not dim the brightness of the present for any human heart with the shadows of old regrets. Do good because of a future which opens possibilities before you, for others, if not for yourselves.

Brethren, friends, all, let us make up our minds that we will be kindly affected one to another in our homes and out of them, on this approaching Christmas day. That the old debate, the ancient strife, the rankling recollection, the sharp contention, shall be put aside, that "envy, hatred, and malice, and all uncharitableness" shall be done away with. Let us forgive and forget; but if we cannot forget let us at least forgive. And so let there be peace between man and man at Christmas—a truce of God.

Let us pray that Love shall come as a little child to our households. That He shall be in our hearts and shall find His expression in all that we do or say on this birthday of goodness and cheer for the world. Then let us resolve that the spirit of the day shall be carried out through our lives, that as Christ did not come for an hour, but for a lifetime, we would fain become as little children on this day of days that we may begin a new life of good will to men.

Let us make this a new birthday of kindness and love that shall endure. That is a Christmas hope, a Christmas wish. Let us give to it the gracious expression of life among men.

From a Far Country

FROM A FAR COUNTRY

Being a New Variation of an Ancient Theme

A STORY FOR GROWN-UPS

I

"*A CERTAIN man had two sons*"—so begins the best and most famous story in the world's literature. Use of the absolute superlative is always dangerous, but none will gainsay that statement, I am sure. This story, which follows that familiar tale afar off, indeed, begins in the same way. And the parallelism between the two is exact up to a certain point. What difference a little point doth make; like the little fire, behold, how great a matter it kindleth! Indeed, lacking that one detail the older story would have had no value; it would not have been told; without its addition this would have been a repetition of the other.

When the modern young prodigal came to himself, when he found himself no longer able to endure the husks of the swine like his ancient exemplar, when he rose and returned to his father because of that distaste, he found no father watching and waiting for him at the end of the road! Upon that change the action of this story hangs. It was a pity, too, because the elder brother was there and in a mood not unlike that of his famous prototype.

Indeed, there was added to that elder brother's natural resentment at the younger's course the blinding power of a great sorrow, for the father of the two sons was dead. He had died of a broken heart. Possessed of no omniscience of mind or vision, he had been unable to foresee the long delayed turning point in the career of his

From a Far Country

younger son and death came too swiftly to enable them to meet again. So long as he had strength, that father had stood, as it were, at the top of the hill looking down the road watching and hoping.

And but the day before the tardy prodigal's return he had been laid away with his own fathers in the God's acre around the village church in the Pennsylvania hills. Therefore there was no fatted calf ready for the disillusioned youth whose waywardness had killed his father. It will be remembered that the original elder brother objected seriously to fatted calves on such occasions. Indeed, the funeral baked meats would coldly furnish forth a welcoming meal if any such were called for.

For all his waywardness, for all his self-will, the younger son had loved his father well, and it was a terrible shock to him (having come to his senses) to find that he had returned too late. And for all his hardness and narrowness the eldest son also had loved his father well—strong tribute to the quality of the dead parent—and when he found himself bereft he naturally visited wrath upon the head of him who he believed rightly was the cause of the untimely death of the old man.

As he sat in the study, if such it might be called, of the departed, before the old-fashioned desk with its household and farm and business accounts, which in their order and method and long use were eloquent of his provident and farseeing father, his heart was hot within his breast. Grief and resentment alike gnawed at his vitals. They had received vivid reports, even in the little town in which they dwelt, of the wild doings of the wanderer, but they had enjoyed no direct communication with him. After a while even rumour ceased to busy itself with the doings of the youth. He had dropped out of their lives utterly after he passed over the hills and far away.

The father had failed slowly for a time, only to break suddenly and swiftly in the end. And the hurried frantic search for the missing had brought no results. Ironically the god of chance had led the young man's repentant footsteps to the door too late.

"Where's father?" cried John Carstairs to the startled woman who stared at him as if she had seen a ghost as, at his knock, she opened the door which he had found locked, not against him, but the hour was late and it was the usual nightly precaution:

"Your brother is in your father's study, sir," faltered the servant at last.

"Umph! Will," said the man, his face changing. "I'd rather see father first."

"I think you had better see Mr. William, sir."

"What's the matter, Janet?" asked young Carstairs anxiously. "Is father ill?"

"Yes, sir! indeed I think you had bettor see Mr. William at once, Mr. John."

Strangely moved by the obvious agitation of the ancient servitor of the house who had known him from childhood, John Carstairs hurried down the long hall to the door of his father's study. Always a scapegrace, generally in difficulties, full of mischief, he had approached that door many times in fear of well merited punishment which was sure to be meted out to him. And he came to it with the old familiar apprehension that night, if from a different cause. He never dreamed that his father was anything but ill. He must see his brother. He stood in no little awe of that brother, who was his exact antithesis in almost everything. They had not got along particularly well. If his father had been inside the door he would have hesitated with his hand on the knob. If his father had not been ill he would not have attempted to face his brother. But his anxiety, which was increased by a sudden foreboding, for Janet, the maid, had looked at him so strangely, moved him to quick action. He threw the door open instantly. What he saw did not reassure him. William was clad in funeral black. He wore a long frock coat instead of the usual knockabout suit he affected on the farm. His face was white and haggard. There was an instant interchange of names.

"John!"

"William!"

And then——

"Is father ill?" burst out the younger. "Janet said——"

"Dead!" interposed William harshly, all his indignation flaming into speech and action as he confronted the cause of the disaster.

"Dead! Good God!"

"God had nothing to do with it."

"You mean?"

"You did it."

"I?"

"Yes. Your drunken revelry, your reckless extravagance, your dissipation with women, your unfeeling silence, your——"

"Stop!" cried the younger. "I have come to my senses. I can't bear it."

"I'll say it if it kills you. You did it, I repeat. He longed and prayed and waited and you didn't come. You didn't write. We could hear nothing. The best father on earth."

The younger man sank down in a chair and covered his face with his hands.

"When?" he gasped out finally.

"Three days ago."

"And have you——"

"He is buried beside mother in the churchyard yonder. Now that you are here I thank God that he didn't live to see what you have become."

The respectable elder brother's glance took in the disreputable younger, his once handsome face marred—one doesn't foregather with swine in the sty without acquiring marks of the association—his clothing in rags. Thus errant youth, that was youth no longer, came back from that far country. Under such circumstances one generally has to walk most of the way. He had often heard the chimes at midnight, sleeping coldly in the straw stack of the fields, and the dust of the road clung to his person. Through his broken shoes his bare feet showed, and he trembled visibly as the other confronted him, partly from hunger and weakness and shattered nerves, and partly from shame and horror and for what reason God only knew.

The tall, handsome man in the long

black coat, who towered over him so grimly stern, was two years older than he, yet to the casual observer the balance of time was against the prodigal by at least a dozen years. However, he was but faintly conscious of his older brother. One word and one sentence rang in his ear. Indeed, they beat upon his consciousness until he blanched and quivered beneath their onslaught.

"Dead—you did it!"

Yes, it was just. No mercy seasoned that justice in the heart of either man. The weaker, self-accusing, sat silent with bowed head, his conscience seconding the words of the stronger. The voice of the elder ran on with growing, terrifying intensity.

"Please stop," interposed the younger. He rose to his feet. "You are right, Will. You were always right and I was always wrong. I did kill him. But you need not have told me with such bitterness. I realized it the minute you said he was dead. It's true. And yet I was honestly sorry. I came back to tell him so, to ask his forgiveness."

"When your money was gone."

"You can say that, too," answered the other, wincing under the savage thrust. "It's as true as the rest probably, but sometimes a man has to get down very low before he looks up. It was that way with me. Well, I've had my share and I've had my fling. I've no business here. Good-bye." He turned abruptly away.

"Don't add more folly to what you have already done," returned William Carstairs, and with the beginnings of a belated pity, he added, "stay here with me, there will be enough for us both and——"

"I can't."

"Well, then," he drew out of his pocket a roll of bills, "take these and when you want more——"

"Damn your money," burst out John Carstairs, passionately. He struck the other's outstretched hand, and in his surprise, William Carstairs let the bills scatter upon the floor. "I don't want it—blood money. Father is dead. I've had mine. I'll trouble you no more."

He turned and staggered out of the room. Now William Carstairs was a proud man and John Carstairs had offended him deeply. He believed all that he had said to his brother, yet there had been developing a feeling of pity for him in his heart, and in his cold way he had sought to express it. His magnanimity had been rejected with scorn. He looked down at the scattered bills on the floor. Characteristically—for he inherited his father's business ability without his heart—he stooped over and picked them slowly up, thinking hard the while. He finally decided that he would give his brother yet another chance for his father's sake. After all, they were brethren. But the decision came too late. John Carstairs had stood not on the order of his going, but had gone at once, none staying him.

William Carstairs stood in the outer door, the light from the hall behind him streaming out into the night. He could see nothing. He called aloud, but there was no answer. He had no idea where his younger brother had gone. If he had been a man of finer feeling or quicker perception, perhaps if the positions of the two had been reversed and he had been his younger brother, he might have guessed that John might have been found beside the newest mound in the churchyard, had one sought him there. But that idea did not come to William, and after staring into the blackness for a long time, he reluctantly closed the door.

Perhaps the vagrant could be found in the morning.

No, there had been no father waiting for the prodigal at the end of the road, and what a difference it had made to that wanderer and vagabond!

II

We leave a blank line on the page and denote thereby that ten years have passed. It was Christmas Eve, that is, it had been Christmas Eve when the little children had gone to bed. Now midnight had passed and it was already Christmas morning. In one of the greatest and most splendid houses on the avenue two little children were nestled all snug in their beds in a nursery. In an adjoining room sound sleep had quieted the nerves of the usually vigilant and watchful nurse. But the little children were wakeful. As always, visions of Santa Claus danced in their heads.

They were fearless children by nature and had been trained without the use of bugaboos to keep them in the paths wherein they should go. On this night of nights they had left the doors of their nursery open. The older, a little girl of six, was startled, but not alarmed, as she lay watchfully waiting, by a creaking sound as of an opened door in the library below. She listened with a beating heart under the coverlet; cause of agitation not fear, but hope. It might be, it must be Santa Claus, she decided. Brother, aged four, was close at hand in his own small crib. She got out of her bed softly so as not to disturb Santa Claus, or— more important at the time—the nurse. She had an idea that Saint Nicholas might not welcome a nurse, but she had no fear at all that he would not be glad to see her.

Need for a decision confronted her. Should she reserve the pleasure she expected to derive from the interview for herself or should she share it with little brother? There was a certain risk in arousing brother. He was apt to awaken clamant, vociferous. Still, she resolved to try it. For one thing, it seemed so selfish to see Santa Claus alone, and for another the adventure would be a little less timorous taken together.

Slipping her feet into her bedroom slippers and covering her nightgown with a little blanket wrap, she tip-toed over to brother's bed. Fortunately, he too was sleeping lightly, and for a like reason. For a wonder she succeeded in arousing him without any outcry on his part. He was instantly keenly, if quietly, alive to the situation and its fascinating possibilities.

"You must be very quiet, John," she whispered. "But I think Santa Claus is down in the library. We'll go down and catch him."

Brother, as became the hardier male, disdained further protection of his small but valiant person. Clad only in his pajamas and his slippers, he followed sister out the door and down the stair. They went hand in hand, greatly excited by the desperate adventure.

What proportion of the millions who dwelt in the great city were children of tender years only statisticians can say, but doubtless there were thousands of little hearts beating with anticipation as the hearts of those children beat, and perhaps there may have been others who were softly creeping downstairs to catch Santa Claus unawares at that very moment.

One man at least was keenly conscious of

one little soul who, with absolutely nothing to warrant the expectation, nothing reasonable on which to base joyous anticipation, had gone to bed thinking of Santa Claus and hoping that, amidst equally deserving hundreds of thousands of obscure children, this little mite in her cold, cheerless garret might not be overlooked by the generous dispenser of joy. With the sublime trust of childhood she had insisted upon hanging up her ragged stocking. Santa Claus would have to be very careful indeed lest things should drop through and clatter upon the floor. Her heart had beaten, too, although she descended no stair in the great house. She, too, lay wakeful, uneasy, watching, sleeping, drowsing, hoping. We may have some doubts about the eternal springing of hope in the human breast save in the case of childhood—thank God it is always verdant there!

III

Now few people get so low that they do not love somebody, and I dare say that no people get so low that somebody does not love them.

"Crackerjack," so called because of his super-excellence in his chosen profession, was, or had been, a burglar and thief; a very ancient and highly placed calling indeed. You doubtless remember that two thieves comprised the sole companions and attendants of the Greatest King upon the most famous throne in history. His sole court at the culmination of His career. "Crackerjack" was no exception to the general rule about loving and being beloved set forth above.

He loved the little lady whose tattered stocking swung in the breeze from the cracked window. Also he loved the wretched woman who with himself shared the honours of parentage to the poor but hopeful mite who was also dreaming of Christmas and the morning. And his love inspired him to action. Singular into what devious courses, utterly unjustifiable, even so exalted and holy an emotion may lead fallible man. Love—burglary! They do not belong naturally in association, yet slip cold, need, and hunger in between and we may have explanation even if there be no justification. Oh, Love, how many crimes are committed in thy name!

"Crackerjack" would hardly have chosen Christmas eve for a thieving expedition if there had been any other recourse. Unfortunately there was none. The burglar's profession, so far as he had practised it, was undergoing a timely eclipse. Time was when it had been lucrative, its rewards great. Then the law, which is no respecter of professions of that kind, had got him. "Crackerjack" had but recently returned from a protracted sojourn at an institution arranged by the State in its paternalism for the reception and harbouring of such as he. The pitiful dole with which the discharged prisoner had been unloaded upon a world which had no welcome for him had been soon spent; even the hideous prison-made clothes had been pawned, and some rags, which were yet the rags of a free man, which had been preserved through the long period of separation by his wife, gave him a poor shelter from the winter's cold.

That wife had been faithful to him. She had done the best she could for herself and baby during the five years of the absence of the bread winner, or in his case the bread taker would be the better phrase. She had eagerly waited the hour of his release; her joy had been soon turned to bitterness. The fact that he had been in prison had shut every door against him and even closed the few that had been open to her. The three pieces of human flotsam had been driven by the wind of adversity and tossed. They knew not where to turn when jettisoned by society.

Came Christmas Eve. They had no money and no food and no fire. Stop! The fire of love burned in the woman's heart, the fire of hate in the man's. Prison life usually completes the education in shame of the unfortunate men who are thrust there. This was before the days in which humane men interested themselves in prisons and prisoners and strove to awaken the world to its responsibilities to, as well as the possibilities of, the convict.

But "Crackerjack" was a man of unusual character. Poverty, remorse, drink, all the things that go to wreck men by forcing them into evil courses had laid him low, and because he was a man originally of education and ability, he had shone as a criminal. The same force of character which made him super-burglar could change him from criminal to man if by chance they could be enlisted in the endeavour.

He had involved the wife he had married in his misfortunes. She had been a good woman, weaker than he, yet she stuck to him. God chose the weak thing to rejuvenate the strong. In the prison he had enjoyed abundant leisure for reflection. After he learned of the birth of his daughter he determined to do differently when he was freed. Many men determine, especially in the case of an ex-convict, but society usually determines better—no, not better, but more strongly. Society had different ideas. It was Brahministic in its religion. Caste? Yes, once a criminal always a criminal.

"Old girl," said the broken man, "it's no use. I've tried to be decent for your sake and the kid's, but it can't be done. I can't get honest work. They've put the mark of Cain on me. They can take the consequences. The kid's got to have some Christmas; you've got to have food and drink and clothes and fire. God, how cold it is! I'll go out and get some."

"Isn't there something else we can pawn?"

"Nothing."

"Isn't there any work?"

"Work?" laughed the man bitterly. "I've tramped the city over seeking it, and you, too. Now, I'm going to get money—elsewhere."

"Where?"

"Where it's to be had."

"Oh, Jack, think."

"If I thought, I'd kill you and the kid and myself."

"Perhaps that would be better," said the woman simply. "There doesn't seem to be any place left for us."

"We haven't come to that yet," said the man. "Society owes me a living and, by God, it's got to pay it to me."

It was an oft-repeated, widely held assertion, whether fallacious or not each may determine for himself.

"I'm afraid," said the woman.

"You needn't be; nothing can be worse than this hell."

He kissed her fiercely. Albeit she was thin and haggard she was beautiful to him. Then he bent over his little girl. He had not yet had sufficient time since his release to get very well acquainted with her. She had been born while he was in prison, but it had not taken any time at all for him to learn to love her. He stared at her a moment. He bent to kiss her and then stopped. He might awaken her. It is always best for the children of the very poor to sleep. He who sleeps dines, runs the

Spanish proverb. He turned and kissed the little ragged stockings instead, and then he went out. He was going to play—was it Santa Claus, indeed?

IV

The strange, illogical, ironical god of chance, or was it Providence acting through some careless maid, had left an area window unlocked in the biggest and newest house on the avenue. Any house would have been easy for "Crackerjack" if he had possessed the open sesame of his kit of burglar's tools, but he had not had a jimmy in his hand since he was caught with one and sent to Sing Sing. He had examined house after house, trusting to luck as he wandered on, and, lo! fortune favoured him.

The clock in a nearby church struck the hour of two. The areaway was dark. No one was abroad. He plunged down the steps, opened the window and disappeared. No man could move more noiselessly than he. In the still night he knew how the slightest sounds are magnified. He had made none as he groped his way through the back of the house, arriving at last in a room which he judged to be the library. Then, after listening and hearing nothing, he ventured to turn the button of a side light in a far corner of the room.

He was in a large apartment, beautifully furnished. Books and pictures abounded, but these did not interest him, although if he had made further examination he might have found things worthy of his attention even there. It so happened that the light bracket to which he had blundered, or had been led, was immediately over a large wall safe. Evidently it had been placed there for the purpose of illuminating the safe door. His eyes told him that instantly. This was greater fortune than he expected. A wall safe in a house like that must contain things of value.

Marking the position of the combination knob, he turned out the light and waited again. The quiet of the night continued unbroken. A swift inspection convinced him that the lock was only an ordinary combination. With proper—or improper—tools he could have opened it easily. Even without tools, such were his delicately trained ear and his wonderfully trained fingers that he thought he could feel and hear the combination. He knelt down by the knob and began to turn it slowly, listening and feeling for the fall of the tumblers. Several times he almost got it, only to fail at the end, but by repeated trials and unexampled patience, his heart beating like a trip-hammer the while, he finally mastered the combination and opened the safe door.

In his excitement when he felt the door move he swung it outward sharply. It had not been used for some time evidently and the hinges creaked. He checked the door and listened again. Was he to be balked after so much success? He was greatly relieved at the absence of sound. It was quite dark in the room. He could see nothing but the safe. He reached his hand in and discovered it was filled with bulky articles covered with some kind of cloth, silver evidently.

He decided that he must have a look and again he switched on the light. Yes, his surmise had been correct. The safe was filled with silver. There was a small steel drawer in the middle of it. He had a broad bladed jack-knife in his pocket and at the risk of snapping the blade he forced the lock and drew out the drawer. It was filled with papers. He lifted the first one and stood staring at it in astonishment, for it was an envelope which bore his name, written by a hand which had long since mouldered away in the dust of a grave.

V

Before he could open the envelope, there broke on his ear a still small voice, not that of conscience, not that of God; the voice of a child—but does not God speak perhaps as often through the lips of childhood as in any other way—and conscience, too?

"Are you Santa Claus?" the voice whispered in his ear.

"Crackerjack" dropped the paper and turned like a flash, knife upraised in his clenched hand, to confront a very little girl and a still smaller boy staring at him in open-eyed astonishment, an astonishment which was without any vestige of alarm. He looked down at the two and they looked up at him, equal bewilderment on both sides.

"I sought dat Santy Claus tame down de chimney," said the younger of the twain, whose pajamas bespoke the nascent man.

"In all the books he has a long white beard. Where's yours?" asked the coming woman.

This innocent question no less than the unaffected simplicity and sincerity of the questioner overpowered "Crackerjack." He sank back into a convenient chair and stared at the imperturbable pair. There was a strange and wonderful likeness in the sweet-faced golden-haired little girl before him to the worn, haggard, and ill-clad little girl who lay shivering in the mean bed in the upper room where God was not—or so he fancied.

"You're a little girl, aren't you?" he whispered.

No voice had been or was raised above a whisper. It was a witching hour and its spell was upon them all.

"Yes."

"What is your name?"

"Helen."

Now Helen had been "Crackerjack's" mother's name and it was the name of his own little girl, and although everybody else called her Nell, to him she was always Helen.

"And my name's John," volunteered the other child.

"John!" That was extraordinary!

"What's your other name?"

"John William."

The man stared again. Could this be coincidence merely? John was his own name and William that of his brother.

"I mean what is your last name?"

"Carstairs," answered the little girl. "Now you tell us who you are. You aren't

"I sought dat Santy Claus tame down de chimney," said the younger of the twain.

Santa Claus, are you? I don't hear any reindeers outside, or bells, and you haven't any pack, and you're not by the fireplace where our stockings are."

"No," said the man, "I'm not exactly Santa Claus, I'm his friend—I——"

What should he say to these children? In his bewilderment for the moment he actually forgot the letter which he still held tightly in his hand.

"Dat's muvver's safe," continued the little boy. "She keeps lots o' things in it. It's all hers but dat drawer. Dat's papa's and——"

"I think I hear some one on the stairs," broke in the little girl suddenly in great excitement. "Maybe that's Santa Claus."

"Perhaps it is," said the man, who had also heard. "You wait and watch for him. I'll go outside and attend to his reindeer."

He made a movement to withdraw, but the girl caught him tightly by the hand.

"If you are his friend," she said, "you can introduce us. You know our names and——"

The golden opportunity was gone.

"Don't say a word," whispered the man quickly. "We 'll surprise him. Be very still."

He reached his hand up and turned out the light. He half hoped he might be mistaken, or that in the darkness they would not be seen, but no. They all heard the footsteps on the stair. They came down slowly, and it was evident that whoever was approaching was using every precaution not to be heard. "Crackerjack" was in a frightful situation. He did not know whether to jerk himself away from the two children, for the boy had clasped him around the leg and the girl still held his hand, or whether to wait.

The power of decision suddenly left him, for the steps stopped before the door. There was a little click as a hand pressed a button on the wall and the whole room was flooded with light from the great electrolier in the centre. Well, the game was up. "Crackerjack" had been crouching low with the children. He rose to his feet and looked straightly enough into the barrel of a pistol held by a tall, severe looking man in a rich silk dressing robe, who confronted him in the doorway. Two words broke from the lips of the two men, the same words that had fallen from their lips when they met ten years before.

"John!" cried the elder man, laying the weapon on a nearby table.

"Will!" answered "Crackerjack" in the same breath.

As if to mark the eternal difference as before, the one was clothed in habiliments of wealth and luxury, the other in the rags and tatters of poverty and shame.

"Why, that isn't Santa Claus," instantly burst out the little girl, "that's papa."

"Dis is Santy Claus's friend, papa," said the little boy. "We were doin' to su'prise him. He said be very still and we minded."

"So this is what you have come to, John," said the elder man, but there was an unwonted gentleness in his voice.

"I swear to God I didn't know it was your house. I just came in here because the window was open."

The other pointed to the safe.

"But you were——"

"Of course I was. You don't suppose I wandered in for fun, do you? I've got a little girl of my own, and her name's Helen, too; our mother's name."

The other brother nodded.

"She's hungry and cold and there's no Christmas for her or her mother."

"Oh, Santy has been here already," cried Master John Williams, running toward the great fireplace, having just that moment discovered the bulging stockings and piles of gifts. His sister made a move in the same direction, for at the other corner hung her stocking and beneath it her pile, but the man's hand unconsciously tightened upon her hand and she stopped.

"I'll stay with you," she said, after a moment of hesitation. "Tell me more about your Helen."

"There's nothing to tell." He released her hand roughly. "You musn't touch me," he added harshly. "Go."

"You needn't go, my dear," said her father quickly. "Indeed, I think, perhaps——"

"Is your Helen very poor?" quietly

asked the little girl, possessing herself of his hand again, "because if she is she can have"—she looked over at the pile of toys—"Well, I'll see. I'll give her lots of things, and——"

"What's this?" broke out the younger man harshly, extending his hand with the letter in it toward the other.

"It is a letter to you from our father."

"And you kept it from me?" cried the other.

"Read it," said William Carstairs.

With trembling hands "Crackerjack" tore it open. It was a message of love and forgiveness penned by a dying hand.

"If I had had this then I might have been a different man," said the poor wretch.

"There is another paper under it, or there should be, in the same drawer," went on William Carstairs, imperturbably. "Perhaps you would better read that."

John Carstairs needed no second invitation. He turned to the open drawer and took out the next paper. It was a copy of a will. The farm and business had been left to William, but one half of it was to be held in trust for his brother. The man read it and then he crushed the paper in his hand.

"And that, too, might have saved me. My God!" he cried, "I've been a drunken blackguard. I've gone down to the very depths. I have been in State's prison. I was, I am, a thief, but I never would have withheld a dying man's forgiveness from his son. I never would have kept a poor wretch who was crazy with shame and who drank himself into crime out of his share of the property."

Animated by a certain fell purpose, he leaped across the room and seized the pistol.

"Yes, and I have you now!" he cried. "I'll make you pay."

He levelled the weapon at his brother with a steady hand.

"What are you doin' to do wif that pistol?" said young John William, curiously looking up from his stocking, while Helen cried out. The little woman acted the better part. With rare intuition she came quickly and took the left hand of the man and patted it gently. For one thing, her father was not afraid, and that reassured her. John Carstairs threw the pistol down again. William Carstairs had never moved.

"Now," he said, "let me explain."

"Can you explain away this?"

"I can. Father's will was not opened until the day after you left. As God is my judge I did not know he had written to you. I did not know he had left anything to you. I left no stone unturned in an endeavour to find you. I employed the best detectives in the land, but we found no trace of you whatever. Why, John, I have only been sorry once that I let you go that night, that I spoke those words to you, and that has been all the time."

"And where does this come from?" said the man, flinging his arm up and confronting the magnificent room.

"It came from the old farm. There was oil on it and I sold it for a great price. I was happily married. I came here and have been successful in business. Half of it all is yours."

"I won't take it."

"John," said William Carstairs, "I offered you money once and you struck it out of my hand. You remember?"

"Yes."

"What I am offering you now is your own. You can't strike it out of my hand. It is not mine, but yours."

"I won't have it," protested the man.

"It's too late. You don't know what I've been, a common thief. 'Crackerjack' is my name. Every policeman and detective in New York knows me."

"But you've got a little Helen, too, haven't you?" interposed the little girl with wisdom and tact beyond her years.

"Yes."

"And you said she was very poor and had no Christmas."

"Yes."

"For her sake, John," said William Carstairs. "Indeed you must not think you have been punished alone. I have been punished, too. I'll help you begin again. Here"—he stepped closer to his brother—"is my hand."

The other stared at it uncomprehendingly.

"There is nothing in it now but affection. Won't you take it?"

Slowly John Carstairs lifted his hand.

From a Far Country 57

His palm met that of his elder brother. He was so hungry and so weak and so overcome that he swayed a little. His head bowed, his body shook and the elder brother put his arm around him and drew him close.

Into the room came William Carstairs' wife. She, too, had at last been aroused by the conversation, and, missing her husband, she had thrown a wrapper about her and had come down to seek him.

"We tame down to find Santy Claus," burst out young John William, at the sight of her, "and he's been here, look muvver."

Yes, Santa Claus had indeed been there. The boy spoke better than he knew.

"And this," said little Helen eagerly, pointing proudly to her new acquaintance, "is a friend of his, and he knows papa and he's got a little Helen and we're going to give her a Merry Christmas."

William Carstairs had no secrets from

his wife. With a flash of womanly intuition, although she could not understand how he came to be there, she divined who this strange guest was who looked a pale, weak picture of her strong and splendid husband, and yet she must have final assurance.

"Who is this gentleman, William?" she asked quietly, and John Carstairs was forever grateful to her for her word that night.

"This," said William Carstairs, "is my father's son, my brother, who was dead and is alive again, and was lost and is found."

And so, as it began with the beginning, this story ends with the ending of the best and most famous of all the stories that were ever told.

On Christmas Giving

ON CHRISTMAS GIVING

Being a Word of Much Needed Advice

CHRISTMAS is the birthday of our Lord, upon which we celebrate God's ineffable gift of Himself to His children. No human soul has ever been able to realize the full significance of that gift, no heart has ever been glad enough to contain the joy of it, and no mind has ever been wise enough to express it. Nevertheless we powerfully appreciate the blessing and would fain convey it fitly. Therefore to commemorate that great gift the custom of exchanging tokens of love and remembrance has grown until it has become well nigh universal. This is a day in which we ourselves crave, as never at any other time, happiness and peace for those we love and that ought to include everybody, for with the angelic message in our ears it should be impossible to hate any one on Christmas day however we may feel before or after.

But despite the best of wills almost inevitably Christmas in many instances has created a burdensome demand. Perhaps by the method of exclusion we shall find out what Christmas should be. It is not a time for extravagance, for ostentation, for vulgar display, it is possible to purchase pleasure for someone else at too high a price to ourselves. To paraphrase Polonius, "Costly thy gift as thy purse can buy, rich but not expressed in fancy, for the gift oft proclaims the man." In making presents observe three principal facts; the length of your purse, the character of your friend, and the universal rule of good taste. Do not plunge into extravagance from which you will

A Christmas Giving

scarcely recover except in months of nervous strain and desperate financial struggle. On the other hand do not be mean and niggardly in your gifts. Oh, not that; avoid selfishness at Christmas, if at no other time. Rather no gift at all than a grudging one. Let your offerings represent yourselves and your affections. Indeed if they do not represent you, they are not gifts at all. "The gift without the giver is bare."

And above all banish from your mind the principle of reciprocity. The *lex talionis* has no place in Christmas giving. Do not think or feel that you must give to someone because someone gave to you. There is no barter about it. You give because you love and without a thought of return. Credit others with the same feeling and be governed thereby. I know one upon whose Christmas list there are over one hundred and fifty people, rich and poor, high and low, able and not able. That man would be dismayed beyond measure if everyone of those people felt obliged to make a return for the Christmas remembrances he so gladly sends them.

In giving remember after all the cardinal principle of the day. Let your gift be an expression of your kindly remembrance, your gentle consideration, your joyful spirit, your spontaneous gratitude, your abiding desire for peace and goodwill toward men. Hunt up somebody who needs and who without you may lack and suffer heart hunger, loneliness, and disappointment.

Nor is Christmas a time for gluttonous eating and drinking. To gorge one's self with quantities of rich and indigestible food is not the noblest method of commemorating the day. The rules and laws of digestion are not abrogated upon the Holy day. These are material cautions, the day has a spiritual significance of which material manifestations are, or ought to be, outward and visible expressions only.

Christmas is one of the great days of obligation in the Church year, then as at Easter if at no other time, Christians should gather around the table of the Lord, kneeling before God's altar in the ministering of that Holy Communion which unites them with the past, the present, and the future—the communion of the saints of God's Holy Church with His Beloved Son. Then and thus in body, soul, and spirit we do truly participate in the privilege and blessing of the Incarnation, then and there we receive that strength which enables everyone of us to become factors in the great extension of that marvellous occurrence throughout the ages and throughout the world.

Let us therefore on this Holy Natal Day, from which the whole world dates its time, begin on our knees before that altar which is at once manger, cross, throne. Let us join thereafter in holy cheer of praise and prayer and exhortation and Christmas carol, and then let us go forth with a Christmas spirit in our hearts resolved to communicate it to the children of men, and not merely for the day but for the future. To make the right use of these our privileges, this it is to save the world.

In this spirit, therefore, so far as poor, fallible human nature permits him to realize it and exhibit it, the author wishes all his readers which at present comprise his only flock—

A MERRY CHRISTMAS AND
A HAPPY NEW YEAR.

It Was the Same Christmas Morning

IT WAS THE SAME CHRISTMAS MORNING

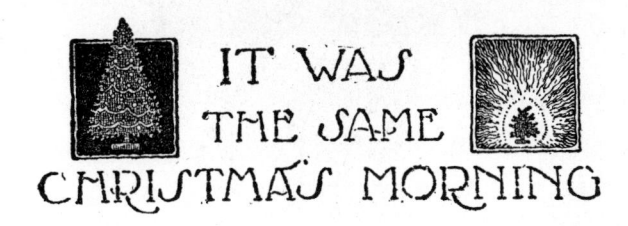

In Which it is Shown how Different the Same Things may Be

A Story for Girls

IN Philadelphia the rich and the poor live cheek by jowl—or rather, back to back.

Between the streets of the rich and parallel to them, run the alleys of the poor. The rich man's garage jostles elbows with the poor man's dwelling.

In a big house fronting on one of the most fashionable streets lived a little girl named Ethel. Other people lived in the big house also, a father, a mother, a butler, a French maid, and a host of other servants. Back of the big house was the garage. Facing the garage on the other side of the alley was a little, old one-story-and-a-half brick house. In this house dwelt a little girl named Maggie. With her lived her father who was a labourer; her mother, who took in washing; and half a dozen brothers, four of whom worked at something or other, while the two littlest went to school.

Ethel and Maggie never played together. Their acquaintance was simply a bowing one—better perhaps, a smiling one. From one window in the big playroom which was so far to one side of the house that Ethel could see past the garage and get a glimpse of the window of the living-room in Maggie's house, the two little girls at first stared at each other. One day Maggie nodded and smiled, then Ethel, feeling very much frightened, for she had been cautioned against playing with or noticing the children in the alley, nodded and smiled back. Now neither of the children felt happy unless they had held

The Same Christmas Morning 71

a pantomimic conversation from window to window at some time during the day.

It was Christmas morning. Ethel awoke very early, as all properly organized children do on that day at least. She had a beautiful room in which she slept alone. Adjacent to it, in another room almost as beautiful, slept Celeste, her mamma's French maid. Ethel had been exquisitely trained. She lay awake a long time before making a sound or movement, wishing it were time to arise. But Christmas was strong upon her, the infection of the season was in her blood. Presently she slipped softly out of bed, pattered across the room, paused at the door which gave entrance to the hall which led to her mother's apartments, then turned and plumped down upon Celeste.

"Merry Christmas," she cried shaking the maid.

To awaken Celeste was a task of some difficulty. Ordinarily the French woman would have been indignant at being thus summarily routed out before the appointed hour but something of the spirit of Christmas had touched her as well. She answered the salutation of the little girl kindly enough, but as she sat up in bed she lifted a reproving finger.

"But," she said, "you mus' keep ze silence, Mademoiselle Ethel. Madame, vôtre maman, she say she mus' not be disturb' in ze morning. She haf been out ver' late in ze night and she haf go to ze bed ver' early. She say you mus' be ver' quiet on ze Matin de Noël!"

"I will be quiet, Celeste," answered the little girl, her lip quivering at the injunction.

It was so hard to be repressed all the time but especially on Christmas Day of all others.

"Zen I will help you to dress immediatement, and zen Villiam, he vill call us to see ze tree."

Never had the captious little girl been more docile, more obedient. Dressing Ethel that morning was a pleasure to Celeste. Scarcely had she completed the task and put on her own clothing when there was a tap on the door.

"Vat is it?"

"Mornin', Miss Celeste," spoke a heavy voice outside, a voice subdued to a decorous softness of tone, "if you an' Miss Ethel are ready, the tree is lit, an'——"

"Ve air ready, Monsieur Villiam," answered Celeste, throwing open the door dramatically.

Ethel opened her mouth to welcome the butler—for if that solemn and portentous individual ever unbent it was to Miss Ethel, whom in his heart of hearts he adored—but he placed a warning finger to his lip and whispered in an awestruck voice:

"The master, your father, came in late last night, Miss, an' he said there must be no noise or racket this morning."

Ethel nodded sadly, her eyes filling at her disappointment; William then marched down the hall with a stately magnificence peculiar to butlers, and opened the door into the playroom. He flung it wide and stood to one side like a grenadier, as Celeste and Ethel entered. There was a gorgeous tree, beautifully trimmed. William had bought the tree and Celeste's French taste had adorned it. It was a sight to delight any child's eyes and the things strewn around it on the floor were even more attractive. Everything that money could buy, that Celeste and William could think of was there. Ethel's mother had given her maid carte

The Same Christmas Morning 75

blanche to buy the child whatever she liked, and Ethel's father had done the same with William. The two had pooled their issue and the result was a toyshop dream. Ethel looked at the things in silence.

"How do you like it, Miss?" asked William at last rather anxiously.

"Mademoiselle is not pleased?" questioned the French woman.

"It—it—is lovely," faltered the little girl.

"We haf selected zem ourselves."

"Yes, Miss."

"Didn't mamma—buy anything—or papa —or Santa?"

"Zey tell us to get vatever you vould like and nevair mind ze money."

"It was so good of you, I am sure," said Ethel struggling valiantly against disappointment almost too great to bear. "Everything is beautiful but—I—wish mamma or papa had—I wish they were here—I'd like them to wish me a Merry Christmas.'

The little lip trembled but the upper teeth came down on it firmly. The child had courage. William looked at Celeste and Celeste shrugged her shoulders, both knowing what was lacking.

"I am sure, Miss, that they do wish you a Merry Christmas, an'"—the butler began bravely, but the situation was too much for him. "There goes the master's bell," he said quickly and turned and stalked out of the room gravely, although no bell had summoned him.

"You may go, Celeste," said Ethel with a dignity not unlike her mother's manner.

The maid shrugged her shoulders again, left the room and closed the door. Everything was lovely, everything was there except that personal touch which means so much even to the littlest girl. Ethel was used

"I am sure, Miss, that they do wish you a Merry Christmas."

The Same Christmas Morning 77

to being cared for by others than her parents but it came especially hard on her this morning. She turned, leaving the beautiful things as they were placed about the tree, and walked to the end window whence she could get a view of the little house beyond the garage over the back wall.

There was a Christmas tree in Maggie's house too. It wouldn't have made a respectable branch for Ethel's tree, and the trimmings were so cheap and poor that Celeste would have thrown them into the waste basket immediately. There were a few common, cheap, perishable little toys around the tree on the floor but to Maggie it was a glimpse of heaven. She stood in her little white night-gown—no such thing as dressing for her on Christmas morning—staring around her. The whole family was grouped about her, even the littlest brothers, who went to school because they were not big enough to work, forgot their own joy in watching their little sister. Her father, her mother, the big boys all in a state of more or less dishevelled undress stood around her, pointing out first one thing and then another which they had been able to get for her by denying themselves some of the necessities of life. Maggie was so happy that her eyes brimmed, yet she did not cry. She laughed, she clapped her hands, and kissed them all round and finally found herself, a big orange in one hand, a tin trumpet in the other, perched upon her father's broad shoulders leading a frantic march around the narrow confines of the living-room. As she passed by the one window she caught a glimpse of the alley. It had been snowing throughout the night and the ground was white.

"Oh," she screamed with delight, "let me see the snow on Christmas morning."

Her father walked over to the window,

The Same Christmas Morning 79

parted the cheap lace curtains, while Maggie clapped her hands gleefully at the prospect. Presently she lifted her eyes and looked toward the other window high up in the air, where Ethel stood, a mournful little figure. Maggie's papa looked too. He knew how cheap and poor were the little gifts he had bought for his daughter.

"I wish," he thought, "that she could have some of the things that child up there has."

Maggie however was quite content. She smiled, flourished her trumpet, waved her orange, but there was no answering smile on Ethel's face now. Finally the wistful little girl in the big house languidly waved her hand, and then Maggie was taken away to be dressed lest she should catch cold after the mischief was done.

"I hope that she's having a nice Christmas," said Maggie, referring to Ethel.

"I hope so too," answered her mother,

wishing that her little girl might have some of the beautiful gifts she knew must be in the great house.

"Whatever she has," said Maggie, gleefully, "she can't have any nicer Christmas than I have, that you and papa and the boys gave me. I'm just as happy as I can be."

Over in the big house, Ethel was also wishing. She was so unhappy since she had seen Maggie in the arms of her big, bearded father, standing by the window, that she could control herself no longer. She turned away and threw herself down on the floor in front of the tree and buried her face in her hands bursting into tears.

It was Christmas morning and she was all alone.

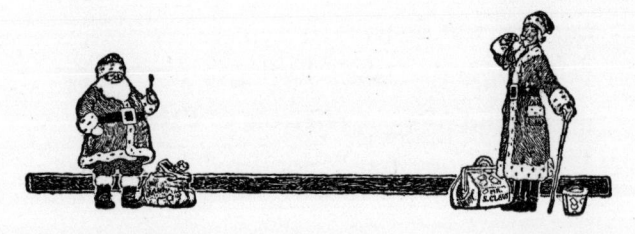

A Christmas Carol

A CHRISTMAS CAROL

"Christmas Then and Now"

The Stars look down
On David's town,
While angels sing in Winter night;
The Shepherds pray,
And far away
The Wise Men follow guiding light.

Little Christ Child
By Mary Mild
In Manger lies without the Inn;
Of Man the Son,
Yet God in One,
To save the lost in World of Sin.

Still stars look down
On David's town
And still the Christ Child dwells with men,
What thought give we
To such as He,
Or souls who live in Sin as then?

Show we our love
To Him above
By offering others' grief to share;
And Christmas cheer
For all the year
Bestow to lighten pain and care.

"The Stars Look Down."

CHRISTMAS CAROL.

Words by
CYRUS TOWNSEND BRADY.

Music by
ALSOP LEFFINGWELL.

The stars look down On Da-vid's town, While an-gels sing in win-ter night. The shep-herds pray And, far a-way, The Wise Men fol-low Guid-ing Light. Lit-tle Christ Child, By Ma-ry Mild, In man-ger lies with-out the inn; Of Man the Son, Yet God in One, To save the lost in

A Christmas Carol

world of sin. Still stars look down on David's town And still the Christ Child dwells with men. What thought give we To such as He, Or souls who live in sin, as then? Show we our love To Him above By off'ring others' grief to share, And Christmas cheer For all the year Bestow to light-en Pain and Care.

The Lone Scout's Christmas

The Lone Scout's Christmas

Wherein is Set Forth the Courage and Resourcefulness of Youth

A Story for Boys

EVERY boy likes snow on Christmas Day, but there is such a thing as too much of it. Henry Ives, alone in the long railroad coach, stared out of the clouded windows at the whirling mass of snow with feelings of dismay. It was the day before Christmas, almost Christmas Eve. Henry did not feel any too happy, indeed he had hard work to keep down a sob. His mother had died but a few weeks before and his father, the captain of a freighter on the Great Lakes, had decided, very reluctantly, to send him to his brother who had a big ranch in western Nebraska.

Henry had never seen his uncle or his aunt. He did not know what kind of people they were. The loss of his mother had been a terrible blow to him and to be separated from his father had filled his cup of sorrow to the brim. His father's work did not end with the close of navigation on the lakes, and he could not get away then although he promised to come and see Henry before the ice broke and traffic was resumed in the spring.

The long journey from the little Ohio town on Lake Erie to western Nebraska had been without mishap. His uncle's ranch lay far away from the main line of the railroad on the end of the branch. There was but one train a day upon it, and that was a mixed train. The coach in which Henry sat was attached to the end of a long string of freight cars. Travel was infrequent in that section of the country. On this day Henry was the only passenger.

A Lone Scout's Christmas

The train had been going up-grade for many miles and had just about reached the crest of the divide. Bucking the snow had become more and more difficult; several times the train had stopped. Sometimes the engine backed the train some distance to get headway to burst through the drift. So Henry thought nothing of it when the car came to a gentle stop.

The all-day storm blew from the west and the front windows of the car were covered with snow so he could not see ahead. Some time before the conductor and rear brakeman had gone forward to help dig the engine out of the drift and they had not come back.

Henry sat in silence for some time watching the whirling snow. He was sad; even the thought of the gifts of his father and friends in his trunk which stood in the baggage compartment of the car did not cheer him. More than all the Christmas gifts in the world, he wanted at that time his mother and father and friends.

"It doesn't look as though it was going to be a very merry Christmas for me," he said aloud at last, and then feeling a little stiff from having sat still so long he got up and walked to the front of the car.

It was warm and pleasant in the coach. The Baker heater was going at full blast and Henry noticed that there was plenty of coal. He tried to see out from the front door; but as he was too prudent to open it and let in the snow and cold he could make out nothing. The silence rather alarmed him. The train had never waited so long before.

Then, suddenly, came the thought that something very unusual was wrong. He must get a look at the train ahead. He ran back to the rear door, opened it and standing

A Lone Scout's Christmas

on the leeward side, peered forward. The engine and freight cars were not there! All he saw was the deep cut filled nearly to the height of the car with snow.

Henry was of a mechanical turn of mind and he realized that doubtless the coupling had broken. That was what had happened. The trainmen had not noticed it and the train had gone on and left the coach. The break had occurred at the crest of the divide and the train had gone rapidly down hill on the other side. The amount of snow told the boy that it would not be possible for the train to back up and pick up the car. He was alone in the wilderness of rolling hills in far western Nebraska. And this was Christmas Eve!

It was enough to bring despair to any boy's heart. But Henry Ives was made of good stuff, he was a first-class Boy Scout and on his scout coat in the trunk were four Merit

Badges. He had the spirit of his father, who had often bucked the November storms on Lake Superior in his great six-hundred-foot freighter, and danger inspired him.

He went back into the car, closed the door, and sat down to think it over. He had very vague ideas as to how long such a storm would last and how long he might be kept prisoner. He did not even know just where he was or how far it was to the end of the road and the town where his uncle's ranch lay.

It was growing dark so he lighted one of the lamps close to the heater and had plenty of light. In doing so he noticed in the baggage rack a dinner pail. He remembered that the conductor had told him that his wife had packed that dinner pail and although it did not belong to the boy he felt justified in appropriating it in such circumstances. It was full of food—eggs, sandwiches, and a bottle of coffee. He was not very hungry but he ate a sandwich. He was even getting cheerful about the situation because he had something to do. It was an adventure.

While he had been eating, the storm had died away. Now he discovered that it had stopped snowing. All around him the country was a hilly, rolling prairie. The cut ran through a hill which seemed to be higher than others in the neighbourhood. If he could get on top of it he might see where he was. Although day was ending it was not yet dark and Henry decided upon an exploration.

Now he could not walk on foot in that deep and drifted snow without sinking over his head under ordinary conditions, but his troop had done a great deal of winter work, and strapped alongside of his big, telescope grip were a pair of snow-shoes which he himself had made, and with the use of which he was thoroughly familiar.

"I mustn't spoil this new suit," he told himself, so he ran to the baggage-room of the car, opened his trunk, got out his Scout uniform and slipped into it in a jiffy. "Glad I ran in that 'antelope dressing race,'" he muttered, "but I'll beat my former record now." Over his khaki coat he put on his heavy sweater, then donned his wool cap and gloves, and with his snow-shoes under his arm hurried back to the rear platform. The snow was on a level with the platform. It rose higher as the coach reached into the cut. He saw that he would have to go down some distance before he could turn and attempt the hill.

He had used his snow-shoes many times in play but this was the first time they had ever been of real service to him. Thrusting his toes into the straps he struck out boldly.

"Thrusting his toes into the straps he struck out boldly."

To his delight he got along without the slightest difficulty although he strode with great care. He gained the level and in ten minutes found himself on the top of the hill, where he could see miles and miles of rolling prairie. He turned himself slowly about, to get a view of the country.

As his glance swept the horizon, at first it did not fall upon a single, solitary thing except a vast expanse of snow. There was not a tree even. The awful loneliness filled him with dismay. He had about given up when, in the last quarter of the horizon he saw, perhaps a quarter of a mile away, what looked like a fine trickle of blackish smoke that appeared to rise from a shapeless mound that bulged above the monotonous level.

"Smoke means fire, and fire means man," he said, excitedly.

The sky was rapidly clearing. A few stars

had already appeared. Remembering what he had learned on camp and trail, he took his bearing by the stars; he did not mean to get lost if he left that hill. Looking back, he could see the car, the lamp of which sent broad beams of light through the windows across the snow.

Then he plunged down the hill, thanking God in his boyish heart for the snow-shoes and his knowledge of them.

It did not take him long to reach the mound whence the smoke rose. It was a sod house, he found, built against a sharp knoll, which no doubt formed its rear wall. The wind had drifted the snow, leaving a half-open way to the door. Noiselessly the boy slipped down to it, drew his feet from the snow-shoes and knocked. There was a burst of sound inside. It made his heart jump, but he was reassured by the fact that the voices were those of children. What they said he could not make out; but, without further ado, he opened the door and entered.

It was a fairly large room. There were two beds in it, a stove, a table, a chest of drawers and a few chairs. From one of the beds three heads stared at him. As each head was covered with a wool cap, drawn down over the ears, like his own, he could not make out who they were. There were dishes on the table, but they were empty. The room was cold, although it was evident that there was still a little fire in the stove.

"Oh!" came from one of the heads in the bed. "I thought you were my father. What is your name?"

"My name," answered the boy, "is Henry Ives. I was left behind alone in the railroad car about a mile back, and saw the smoke from your house and here I am."

"Have you brought us anything to burn?" asked the second head.

"Or anything to eat?" questioned the third.

"My name is Mary Wright," said the first speaker, "and these are my brothers George and Philip. Father went away yesterday morning with the team, to get some coal and some food. He went to Kiowa."

"That's where I am going," interrupted Henry.

"Yes," continued Mary, "I suppose he can't get back because of the snow. It's an awful storm."

"We haven't anything to eat, and I don't know when father will be back," said George.

"And it's Christmas Eve," wailed Philip, who appeared to be about seven.

He set up a howl about this which his brother George, who was about nine, had great difficulty in quieting.

"We put the last shovelful of coal in the stove," said Mary Wright, "and got into bed to keep warm."

"I'll go outside while you get up and dress," said Henry considerately, "and then we will try and get to the car. It is warm there, and there is something to eat."

"You needn't go," said the girl; "we are all dressed." She threw back the covers and sprang out of bed. She was very pretty and about Henry's own age, he discovered, although she was pale and haggard with cold and hunger.

"Goody, goody!" exclaimed little Philip, as his feet landed on the floor. "Maybe we'll have some Christmas, too."

"Maybe we will," said Henry, smiling at him. "At least we will have something to eat."

"Well, let's start right away then," urged George.

This brought Henry face to face with a dilemma. "I have only one pair of snow-shoes," he said at last, "and you probably don't know how to use them anyway, and you can't walk on the snow."

"I have a sled," suggested George.

"That won't do," said Henry. "I've got to have something that won't sink in the snow—that will lie flat, so I can draw you along."

"How about that table?" said the girl.

"Good suggestion," cried Henry.

It was nothing but a common kitchen table. He turned it upside down, took his Scout axe from its sheath, knocked the legs off, fastened a piece of clothesline to the butts of two of them.

"Now if I could have something to turn up along the front, so as not to dig into the snow," he said, "it would be fine." He

A Lone Scout's Christmas

thought a moment. "Where is that sled of yours, George?"

"Here," said George, dragging it forth. The runners curved upwards. Henry cut them off, in spite of Philip's protests. He nailed these runners to the front of the table and stretched rope tightly across them so that he had four up-curves in front of the table.

"Now I want something to stretch on these things, so as to let the sled ride over the snow, instead of digging into it," he said to the girl.

She brought him her father's old "slicker." Henry cut it into suitable shape and nailed and lashed it securely to the runners and to the table top. Now he had a flat-bottomed sled with a rising front to it that would serve. He smiled as he looked at the queer contrivance and said aloud: "I wish Mr. Lesher could see that!"

"Who is Mr. Lesher?" asked George.

"Oh, he's my Scoutmaster back in Ohio. Now come on!"

He opened the door, drew the sled outside, pushed it up on the snow and stepped on it. It bore his weight perfectly.

"It's all right," he cried. "But it won't take all three of you at once."

"I'll wait," said Mary, "you take the two boys."

"Very well," said Henry.

"You'll surely come back for me?"

"Surely, and I think it's mighty brave of you to stay behind. Now come on, boys," he said.

Leaving Mary filled with pleasure at such praise, he put the two boys carefully into the sled, stepped into his snow-shoes and dragged them rapidly across the prairie. It was quite dark now, but the sky was clear and the stars were bright. The storm had

A Lone Scout's Christmas

completely stopped. He remembered the bearings he had taken by the stars, and reached the high hill without difficulty. Below him lay the car.

Presently he drew up before the platform. He put the boys in the car, told them to go up to the fire and warm themselves and not to touch anything. Then he went back for the girl.

"Did you think I was not coming?" he asked as he re-entered the cabin.

"I knew you would come back," said the girl and it was Henry's turn to tingle with pride.

He wrapped her up carefully, and fairly ran back to the car. They found the boys warm and comfortable and greatly excited.

"If we just had a Christmas tree and Santa Claus and something to eat and a drink of water and a place to sleep," said the youngest boy, "it would be great fun."

"I am afraid we can't manage the Christmas tree," said Henry, "but we can have everything else."

"Do you mean Santy?"

"Santy too," answered the boy. "First of all, we will get something to eat."

"We haven't had anything since morning," said the girl. Henry divided the sandwiches into three portions. As it happened, there were three hard-boiled eggs. He gave one portion to each of his guests.

"You haven't left any for yourself," said Mary.

"I ate before I looked for you," answered Henry, although the one sandwich had by no means satisfied his hunger.

"My, but this is good!" said George.

"Our mother is dead," said Mary Wright after a pause, "and our father is awful poor. He has taken out a homestead and we are trying to live on it until he gets it proved up. We have had a very hard time since mother died."

"Yes, I know," said Henry, gravely; "my mother died, too."

"I wonder what time it is?" asked the girl at last.

Henry pulled out his watch. "It is after six o'clock," he said.

"Say," broke in George, "that's a funny kind of a uniform you've got on."

"It is a Boy Scout uniform."

"Oh, is it?" exclaimed George. "I never saw one before. I wish I could be a Scout!"

"Maybe you can," answered Henry. "I am going to organize a troop when I get to Kiowa. But now I'm going to fix beds for you. Of course we are all sleepy after such a hard day."

He had seen the trainmen lift up the bottoms of the seats and lay them lengthwise of the car. He did this, and soon made four fairly comfortable beds. The two nearest the stove he gave to the boys. He indicated the next one was for Mary, and the one further down toward the middle of the car was for himself.

"You can all go to bed right away," he said when he had made his preparations. The two boys decided to accept this advice. Mary said she would stay up a little longer and talk with Henry.

"You can't undress," she said to the two boys. "You'll have to sleep as you are." She sat down in one of the car seats; Philip knelt down at one knee and George at the other. The girl, who was barely fifteen had already taken her mother's place. She laid her hand on each bent head and listened while one after the other the boys said their prayers. She kissed them good-night, saw them comfortably laid out on the big cushions with their overcoats for pillows and turned away.

A Lone Scout's Christmas 109

"Say," began Philip, "you forgot something, Mary."

"What have I forgotten, dear?"

"Why, it's Christmas Eve and we must hang up our stockings."

Mary threw up her hands. "I am afraid this is too far away for Santa Claus. He won't know that we are out here," she said.

"Oh, I don't know," said Henry, thinking rapidly, "let them hang them up."

Mary looked at him in surprise. "They haven't any to hang up," she said. "We can't take those they're wearing."

"You should have thought of that," wailed Philip, "before you brought us here."

"I have some extra ones in my bag," said Henry. "We will hang them up."

He opened the bag and brought out three stockings, one for each of his guests. He fastened them to the baggage racks above the seats and watched the two boys contentedly close their eyes and go to sleep.

"They will be awfully disappointed when they wake up in the morning and do not find anything in them," said Mary.

"They're going to find something in them," said Henry confidently.

He went to the end of the car, opened his trunk and lifted out various packages which had been designed for him. Of course he was going on sixteen, but there were some things that would do for Philip and plenty of things for George and some good books that he had selected himself that would do for Mary. Then there were candy and nuts and cakes and oranges galore. Mary was even more excited than he was as they filled the boys' stockings and arranged things that were too big to go in them.

"These are your own Christmas gifts, I

know," said the girl, "and you haven't hung up your stocking."

"I don't need to. I have had my Christmas present."

"And what is that?"

"A chance to make a merry Christmas for you and your little brothers," answered Henry, and his heart was light.

"How long do you suppose we will have to stay here?" asked the girl.

"I don't know. I suppose they will try to dig us out to-morrow. Meanwhile we have nuts, oranges, crackers, and little cakes, to say nothing of the candy, to live on. Now you go to bed and have a good sleep."

"And what will you do?"

"I'll stay up for a while and read one of these books and keep the fire going."

"You are awfully good to us," said Mary, turning away. "You are just like a real Santa Claus."

"We have to help other people—especially people in trouble," answered the boy. "It is one of the first Scout rules. I am really glad I got left behind and found you. Good-night."

The girl, whose experience that day had been hard, soon fell asleep with her brothers. Henry did not feel sleepy at all; he was bright and happy and rejoiced. This certainly *was* an adventure. He wondered what Dick and Joe and Spike and the other fellows of his troop would think when he wrote them about it. He did not realize that he had saved the lives of the children, who would assuredly have frozen to death in the cabin.

When he was satisfied that Mary was sound asleep, he put some things in her stocking and then piled in the rack over her head two books he thought the girl would like. It was late when he went to

A Lone Scout's Christmas

sleep himself, happier than he had dreamed he could be.

He awoke once in the night to replenish the fire, but he was sleeping soundly at seven o'clock in the morning when the door of the car opened and half a dozen men filed in. They had not made any noise. Even the big snow-plough tearing open the way from Kiowa had not disturbed the four sleepers.

The first man in was the conductor. After the trainmen had discovered that the coach had been left behind they had managed to get into Kiowa and had started back at once with the rotary plough to open the road and to rescue the boy. Henry's uncle had been in town to meet Henry, and of course the trainmen let him go back with them on the plough. The third man was Mr. Wright. He had been caught by the storm and, as he said, the abandoned coach must be near his claim, he asked to be taken along because he was afraid his children would be freezing to death.

The men stopped and surveyed the sleeping boys and girl. Their glances ranged from the children to the bulging stockings and the pile of Christmas presents in the racks.

"Well, can you beat that?" said the conductor.

"By George!" exclaimed Rancher Ives, "a regular Christmas layout!"

"These are my children safe and well, thank God!" cried Mr. Wright.

"Boy," said the conductor, laying his hand on Henry's shoulder, "we came to wish you a Merry Christmas."

"Father!" cried Mary Wright, awakened by the voice, and the next minute she was in his arms, while she told him rapidly what Henry had done for them all.

A Lone Scout's Christmas

The boys were awake, too, but humanity had no attraction for them.

"Santa has come!" shouted Philip making a dive for his stocking.

"This is your uncle, Jim Ives," said the conductor to Henry.

"And this is my father," said Mary in turn.

"I am awfully sorry," said Henry to the conductor, "but we had to eat your dinner. And I had to chop up your kitchen table," he added, turning to Mr. Wright.

"I am glad there was something to eat in the pail," said one.

"You could have chopped the cabin down," said the other.

"By George!" said the ranchman proudly. "I wrote to your father to send you out here and we'd make a man of you, but it seems to me you are a man already," he continued as Mary Wright poured forth the story of their rescue.

"No, I am not a man," said Henry to his uncle, as he flushed with pride at the hearty praise of these men. "I am just a——"

"Just a what?" asked the conductor as the boy hesitated.

"Why, just a Boy Scout," answered Henry.

The LONE SCOUT'S CHRISTMAS

Looking into the Manger

LOOKING INTO THE MANGER

A Christmas Meditation

CHRISTMAS morning, the day we celebrate as the anniversary of the birth of our Lord and Saviour, Jesus Christ, in the obscure, little hill town of Bethlehem in the far-off Judæan land, over nineteen hundred years ago!

It is said:

"When beggars die, there are no comets seen:
  The heavens themselves blaze forth the death of princes."

What is true of the passing of kings is perhaps more true of their coming; yet in this birth are singular contradictions. The Child was born a beggar. There lacks no touch which even imagination could supply to indicate the meanness of His earthly condition. Homeless, His mother, save for the stable of the public inn—and words can hardly describe any place more unsuited—was shelterless, unprotected, in that hour of travail pain.

I love to let my imagination dwell upon that scene. Sometimes I think wayfarers may have gathered in the tavern hard by and with music and play sought to while away the hours as travellers have from time immemorial. Perhaps in some pause in their merriment, a strange cry of anguish, borne by the night wind from the rude shelter without, may have stopped their revelry for a moment and one may have asked of another:

"What is that?"

The servant of the house who stood obsequious to promote their pleasure may have answered apologetically:

Looking into the Manger

"It is the cry of a woman of the people in travail in the inn yard."

I can fancy their indifference to the answer, or I can hear perhaps the rude jest, or the vulgar quip, with which such an announcement may have been received, as the play or the music went on again.

Oh, yes, the world in solemn stillness lay, doubtless, that winter night, but not the people in it. They pursued their several vocations as usual. They loved or they hated, they worked or they played, they hoped or they despaired, they dreamed or they achieved, just as they had done throughout the centuries, just as they have done since that day, just as they will do far into the future; although their little God came to them, as never He came before, in the stable in the Bethlehem hills that night.

And yet, had they but cast their eyes

upward like the wise men—it is always your wise man who casts his eyes upward—they, too, might have seen the star that blazed overhead. It was placed so high above the earth that all men everywhere could see to which spot on the surface it pointed. Or, had they been devout men, they would have listened for heavenly voices—it is always your devout man who tries to hear other things than the babble of the Babel in which he lives—they, too, could have heard the angelic chorus like the shepherds in the fields and on the hillsides that frosty night.

For the heavens did blaze forth the birth of the Child. Not with the thunder of guns, not with the blare of trumpets, not with the beating of drums, not with the lighting of castle, village, and town, the kindling of beacons upon the far-flung hills, the cry of fast-riding messengers through the night,

Looking into the Manger

and the loud acclaim of thousands which greet the coming of an earthly king, was He welcomed; but by the still shining of a silent star and by the ineffable and transcendent voices of an Angel Choir.

How long did the Shepherds listen to that chorus? How long did it ring over the hills and far away? Whither went the Wise Men? Into what dim distance vanished the star?

> "Where are the roses of yesterday?
> What has become of last year's snow?"

And the residuum of it all was a little Baby held to a woman's breast in a miserable hovel in the most forlorn and detested corner of the world. And yet to-day and at this hour, and at every hour during the twenty-four, men are looking into that chamber; men are bowing to that Child and His mother, and even that mother is at the feet of the Child.

From the snow peaks of the North land, "from Greenland's icy mountains to India's coral strand," and on and on through all the burning tropics to the companion ice of the other pole, the antarctic, and girdling the world from east to west as well, the adoration continues. It comes alike from the world's noblest, from the world's highest, from the world's truest, from the world's kindest, from the world's poorest, from the world's humblest, from the world's best.

Do not even the soldiers in the trenches upon the far-flung battle lines pause to listen, look to see as for a moment dies away the cannonade? Do not even the sailors of war and trade peer across the tossing waters of the great deep, longing for a truce of God if only for an hour upon this winter morning?

Yes, they all look into the manger as they look upon the cross and if only for an instant this war reddened planet comes to

"The world bows down to a Mother and her Child—and the Mother herself is at the feet of the Child."

"*see and believe.*" What keen vision saw in the Baby the Son of God and the Son of Man? What simple faith can see these things in Him now? "*Let us now go even unto Bethlehem and see this thing which is come to pass.*"

That birth is known as the Incarnation. Ye know not "*how the bones do grow in the womb of her that is with child.*" Life itself is insusceptible of any definition which satisfies, but we know that we live, nevertheless. Science points out a common origin in protoplasmic cells and is quite unable to explain so common a fact as sex differentiation. I care not what methods of accounting for life you propose, you yet have to refer it to the Author of all life "*in whom we live and move and have our being.*" Why, therefore, should the Incarnation be thought incredible or impossible because it does not come within the limitations of our present understanding and it is not taught by our limited human experience. The sweet reasonableness of the Incarnation, this conception by Divine power, this birth from the Virgin mother, should appeal to all who think deeply on these subjects.

And yet perhaps the manner, place, and circumstance of this birth may awaken wonder. Possibly you would have the King come as other kings come, in pomp and circumstance, glory and majesty, with heralds preceding, music playing, blossoms strewn, and people cheering. Oh, no, that way did not seem the best way to the wisdom of God—a young girl, an old man, in the stable, no other tendance, no luxury, no comfort—poverty, humility, absolute.

Let us forget the Angel Chorus and the blazing star and go now even unto Bethlehem and look into the manger at that Child, while the uncomprehending cattle stare resentful perhaps at their displacement. The King comes as a Child, as weak, as helpless, as vocal of its pains as any other child. Not a Child of luxury, not a Child of consequence, not a Child of comfort, but a Child of poverty; and in the eyes of the blind world, if they had been privy to it, without the glorious vision of the good man, Joseph, a Child of shame! If the world had known that the Babe was not the Child of Joseph and Mary how it would have mocked. What laughter, what jeers, what contempt, what obloquy, what scorn would have been heaped upon the woman's head! Why the world would heap them there now were it not that that portion of it which disbelieves in the Incarnation, says that Joseph was after all the father of the Child.

Nor shall we go down to Bethlehem alone. The poor, ignorant shepherds came to the cradle that night. They could understand.

It did not seem strange to them that their God was poor, for they themselves were poor. I wonder how much the shepherds reflected. Theirs is a profession which gives rise to thought; they are much alone in the waste places with the gentlest of God's creatures. Their paths lead by green pastures and still waters; they enjoy long, lonely hours for meditation. Did they say:

"Ah! God has come to us as a poor man, not because there is anything particularly noble or desirable in poverty, but because so many of us are so very poor, and because the most of us have been poor all the time, and because it is probable that most of us will be poor in the future!"

Many a poor man has looked up into the silent heavens and wondered sometimes whether God understood or cared about his wretched lot. Of course God always knew and cared, we cannot gainsay that, but in order

Looking into the Manger 129

to make men know that He knew and to make them believe that He cared, He let them see that He did not disdain to be a poor man and humble; that He sought His followers and supporters in the great majority. *My God was a Carpenter!* That is why He came to the stable; that is why He came to the manger. And that is why the poor come to Him.

And there came to that same cradle, a little while after, the Wise Men. They were professional wise men; they belonged to the learned, the cultured, the thoughtful class; but they were wise men as well in the sense in which we use wisdom to-day. That is, they looked beyond earthly conditions and saw Divinity where the casual glance does not see it. How many a seamed, rugged face, how many a burden-bent back, how many a faltering footstep, how many a knotted, calloused hand is perhaps more nearly in the image of God than the fairer face, the straighter figure, the softer palm!

The shepherds were not only poor, but they laboured in their poverty; they were working men and they worshipped Him, the Working Man. The wise men were not only wise, but they were rich. They brought the treasures of the earth from the ends thereof and laid them before the Babe and the mother. How fragrant the perfume of the frankincense and the myrrh, and how rich the lustre of the gold and silver in the mean surroundings of the hovel. They took no thought of their costly apparel, they had no fear of contamination from their surroundings, no question of relative degree entered their heads. As simply and as truly as the shepherds they worshipped the Christ. The rich and the poor met together there, and the Lord was the maker of them all.

Was that baby-hand the shaper of destiny? Was that working-hand the director of events? Even so. The Lord's power is not less the Lord's power though it be not exhibited in the stretched out arm of majesty.

Some of you who read this and many more who can not are poor, perhaps very poor, but you can stand beside that manger and look at that Baby's face, you can reflect upon the Child, how He grew, what He said, what He did, until a cross casts its black shadow across your vision—the war is raising many crosses and many there be that walk the *via dolorosa* to them to-day. You shall be counted blessed if you can gaze at that cross until it is transformed by the glory of the resurrection. And in it all you can see your God —the poor man's God!—the rich man's God!—everybody's God!

You can know that your God was poor, that He was humble, that He struggled under adverse conditions, that He laboured, that He was hungry, thirsty, tired, cold, that He was homeless, that He was denied many of the joys of human society and the solace of affection, that His best friends went back on Him, that everybody deserted Him, and that the whole world finally rose up and crushed Him down. That he suffered all things. Only a very great God could so endure. Only one who was truly God could so manifest Himself in pain.

You can understand how He can comprehend what your trouble is. Oh, yes, the poor and the bereaved have as great a right to look into that manger and see their God there as have the rich and the care free.

Now there is a kind of pernicious socialism which condemns riches as things unholy and exalts poverty as a thing acceptable to God. That Baby came as well to the rich as to the poor. Do not forget that. It is not generally understood, but it is true. He accepted gladly the hospitality, the alms, the gifts, priceless in value, of those who had great possessions and He loved them even as He loved those who had nothing. The rich and wise also have a right to look into that cradle to see their God, too. When we say He is the God of all classes we do not mean that He is only the God of the poor any more than we mean He is only the God of the rich.

He came to all the children of men and they can all stand by that cradle this morning and claim Him as their own; ask, receive, and share in His blessing. The light that shone in the darkness lighted impartially the world. Some of you are blessed with competences and some of the competences are greater than others. What of it? The poor man may serve God acceptably in his poverty and the rich man may serve God acceptably in his wealth. There is one God and though He is King of Kings and Lord of Lords, even though He may lie lowly in a manger, yet the kingdom of Heaven is like a republic—it is a democracy in which all are equal, or if there be distinctions they are based on righteousness alone —saving only the distinctions Divine.

Now there is one other condition into which all men inevitably fall. Whether they be rich or whether they be poor, they are all bound to be sorrowful. Sooner or later, we are certain to be troubled. And that is more true today, doubtless, than in any other period in the long history of this old world.

These sorrowful ones can go unto Bethlehem and look into the cradle and claim the Child as their God. For every sorrow that has been yours, He experienced; every grief that you have bowed before, He was forced to struggle with. Very tender and

Looking into the Manger

compassionate is our Lord. I am quite sure that He notices your bowed head, that He puts His arms across your shoulders, that He whispers words of comfort into your ear, or that He gives you the silent sympathy of His presence, that He takes you by the hand; that whatever action most appeals to you and is best for you He takes if you wish Him to.

There are many people belonging to you or your family who are far away, whom you would fain have with you this Christmas morning. Many of them are fighting manfully in His cause, too. Do not forget that our Lord came to the family! that He made a family by coming. These far-off loved ones are doing what we are doing this morning. And there are some you love who are still farther away. The sound of their earthly voices is stilled, we may not clasp their hands, we cannot see them any more. They are gone from the world, but not from our hearts. If they are not here I think they are with Him. And we may be sure that it is very pleasant to them where He is. They are not unmindful of our human regrets and longings, but I think we ought not to be unmindful of their peaceful joy in His presence.

And so everybody has a right to come to that cradle, the poor, the humble, the hard workers, the toilers, the wise, the learned, the easy, the rich, the joyous, the sad, the sorrowful, the bereaved. They may all look into the manger and see their God.

He came to a family; He made a family. We are all in that family, the children of the selfsame Father, the sons of the selfsame God, the brethren of Him of the manger—German and French, English and Austrian, Italian and Bulgar, Russian and Turk! Ay, and above all and with all American and

Belgian. Sirs, we be, not twelve, but many brethren! What does that mean?

There is one musical word with, I think, perhaps the ugliest meaning in the language. It is *rancour*. Let us do away with it, let us put it aside. If we are poor let us be brethren to the other poor, if we are rich let us be brethren to the other rich, if we are wise let us be brethren to the other wise, if we are foolish let us be brethren to the other foolish. Ah, that is not difficult; it is an easy task. But that is not enough. Brotherhood is broader, thank God! Let the poor be brethren to the rich and the rich to the poor, the wise to the ignorant, the misguided to the well-directed, the ignorant to the wise, the foolish to the discreet, the discreet to the foolish, the glad to the sorrowful, the sorrowful to the glad, the servants of the Lord to the sinners against Him!

"Then none was for a party;
  Then all were for the state;
Then the great man helped the poor,
  And the poor man loved the great:
Then lands were fairly portioned;
  Then spoils were fairly sold:
The Romans were like brothers,
  In the brave days of old."

Let us make out of the old pagan ideals present-day realities in our hearts as we go even unto Bethlehem and look into the cradle of the King; realities in His own nobler and better words:

"Jesus answered and said unto them, Go and shew John again those things which ye do hear and see: the blind receive their sight, and the lame walk, the lepers are cleansed, and the deaf hear, the dead are raised up, and the poor have the gospel preached to them. And blessed is he whosoever shall not be offended in Me."

Peace, goodwill toward men! Peace to men of goodwill! That is what the angels sang. But there is nothing on earth to prevent us from making it our human song as well. As we stand by the cradle of the Master and peer into the manger at that which every human being loves, a baby, our earthly differences of nationality, of rank, power, station, and influence—things that are but the guinea's stamp upon the gold of character and personality—fade into insignificance and become as nothing. The little child in life notices none of these distinctions, he marks nothing of them. Let us come as little children before Him. We may be war-battered, sin-marked, toil-stained, care-burdened. Let us forget it all this Christmas morning.

It was a poor place, that manger—the poorest place on earth—but it was a place. It was somewhere. Let us give humanity even as little as a manger. Let us not take up the Christ Child as we see Him and throw

Him out into the streets, or into no man's land. That is what we do when we mock Him, when we deny Him, when we laugh Him to scorn. Let us not shut Him out of His home place in our souls. Let us not refuse to open when His hand knocks upon the door. That is what we do when we are indifferent to Him. Let us take him out of the manger cradle, each one of us, and enthrone Him in the most precious place we have, our inmost hearts.

It all happened a very long time ago and much water has run in the brooks of the world under the bridges thereof since that time, but the mangers of the world are never empty. They are always full. In one sense, Christ is being born everywhere at this very hour and at all hours.

Let us give the Child the best we have, the best we can. Let us even now go down unto Bethlehem, laden with what we have for the use of the King, and let us see in every child of man that lacks anything this Christmas morning the image of Him who in that manger lay in Bethlehem and let us minister to their needs in love.

"The little Christ is coming down*
   Across the fields of snow;
The pine trees greet Him where they stand,
The willows bend to kiss His hand,
The mountain laurel is ablush
In hidden nooks; the wind, ahush
And tiptoe, lest the violets wake
Before their time for His sweet sake;
The stars, down dropping, form a crown
   Upon the waiting hills below—
The little Christ is coming down
   Across the fields of snow.

*These loving and appealing verses were written by Harriet F. Blodgett, of whom unfortunately I know absolutely nothing but her name. I am sure, however, that if they had been written today another verse, even more touching than those I have quoted, would have been inspired by present conditions. And we should have seen "The Little Christ" coming down between the lines in Flanders, on the Balkan Frontier, amid the snows of Russia and the deserts of Mesopotamia, and perhaps, as of old, even walking on the waters in the midst of the sea.

The little Christ is coming down
   Across the city streets;
The wind blows coldly from the north,
His dimpled hands are stretching forth,
And no one knows and no one cares,
The priests are busy with their prayers,
The jostling crowd hastes on apace,
And no one sees the pleading face,
None hears the cry as through the town
   He wanders with His small cold feet—
The little Christ is coming down
   Across the city streets."

What welcome shall we have for Him, my friends?

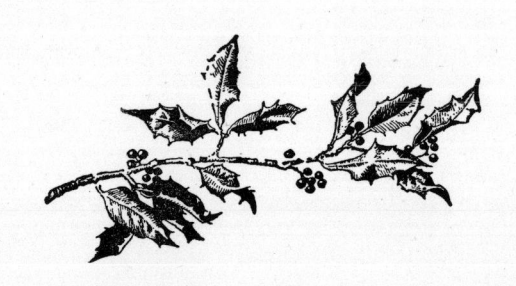

Christmas in the Snows

CHRISTMAS IN THE SNOWS

Being Some Personal Adventures in the Far West.*

THE love of Christmas is as strong in the West as it is in any section of the country—perhaps, indeed, stronger, for people who have few pleasures cherish holidays more highly than those for whom many cheap amusements are provided. But when the manifestation of the Christmas spirit is considered, there is a great difference between the West and the East. There are vast

---

*This bit of personal history is reprinted from my book *Recollections of a Missionary in the Great West* by the courtesy of Messrs. Charles Scribner's Sons, the publishers thereof. Incidentally the reader will find much interesting matter in the way of reminiscence and anecdote in that little volume, should he chance upon it.

sections of country in which evergreens do not grow and to which it would not pay to ship them; consequently Christmas trees are not common, and therefore they are the more prized when they may be had. There are no great rows nor small clusters of inviting shops filled with suggestive and fascinating contents at attractive prices. The distances from centres of trade are so great that the things which may be purchased even in the smallest towns in more favourable localities for a few cents

---

There are some amusing things connected with the publication in serial form of these episodes. The great magazine in which it appeared has very strong views on certain subjects. Following out a policy which has deservedly won them perhaps the largest circulation of any magazine in the world it seemed to the editors necessary and desirable to make some changes in the story as originally written and as it appears hereafter.

For instance the revised serial version made the cowboy lift the flask of whiskey to his lips and then it declared that after a long look at the sleeping children he put it down! I was quite agreeable to the change. I remember remarking that the cowboy certainly did "put it down." It was a way cowboys had in those bygone days; so the editor and the author were both satisfied.

have there almost a prohibitive price put upon them. The efforts of the people to give their children a merry Christmas in the popular sense, however, are strong and sometimes pitiful.

It must not be forgotten that the West is settled by Eastern people, and that no very great difference exists between them save for the advantages presented by life in the West for the higher development of character. Western people are usually brighter,

---

Another amusing thing I recall in connection with the serial publication was this: The art editor of the magazine wrote to the officials of the railroad, the name of which I gave in the first version but which I now withhold, saying that the magazine had a story of a snow-bound train on the railroad in question and asking for pictures of snow-bound trains to help the artist illustrate it. By return mail came an indignant remonstrance almost threatening a lawsuit because the railroad in question, one of the southerly transcontinental roads, made a point in its appeal to travellers that its trains were never snow-bound! The art editor who was not without a vein of humour wrote back and asked if they could furnish him with pictures of snow-bound trains on competing roads and they sent him a box full!

C. T. B.

quicker, more progressive and less conservative, and more liberal than those from whom they came. The survival of the fittest is the rule out there and the qualities of character necessary to that end are brought to the top by the strenuous life necessitated by the hardships of the frontier. If the people are not any better than they were, it is because they are still clinging to the obsolete ideas of the East.

The Eastern point of view always reminds me of the reply of the bishop to the layman who was deploring the poor quality of the clergy. "Yes," said the bishop, "some of them are poor; but consider the stock from which they come. You see, we have nothing but laymen out of which to make them."

The East never understands the West— the real West that is, which lies beyond the Mississippi, the Missouri, and the Rocky Mountains. They know nothing of its ideas, its capacities, its possibilities, its educational facilities, its culture, its real power, in the East. And they do not wish to learn, apparently. The Easterners fatuously think, like Job, that they are the people, and wisdom will die with them. Some years since an article in the "Forum" on the theme, "Kansas more civilized than New York" conclusively proved the proposition to the satisfaction of the present writer at least.

Yet I know numberless dwellers in Gotham whose shibboleth is "nothing outside of New York City but scenery," and they are a little dubious about admitting that. When one describes the Grand Canyon or the Royal Gorge they point to Nassau or Wall Street, and the Woolworth tower challenges Pike's Peak!

I sat at a dinner table one day when the salted almonds were handed me with the remark: "I suppose you never saw anything like these out West. Try some." And my wife has been quite gravely asked if we feared any raids by the Indians and if they troubled us by their marauding in Kansas. I have found it necessary to inform the curious that we did not live in tepees or wigwams when in Nebraska or Colorado.

Shortly after I came East to live I was talking with a man and a very stupid man at that, who informed me that he graduated from Harvard; to which surprising statement he added the startling information, for the benefit of my presumably untutored occidental mind, that it was a college near Boston! They have everything in the West that the East has so far as their sometimes limited means will provide them and when they have no money they have patience, endurance, grim determination, and courage, which are better than money in the long run.

The cities and smaller towns especially

as a rule are cleaner, better governed, more progressive, better provided with improvements and comforts than corresponding places in the East. Scarcely a community exists without its water works, electric light plant, telephone system, trolleys, paved streets, etc. Of course, this does not apply to the extreme frontier in which my field of work largely lay so many years ago. The conditions were different there—the people too in that now far-distant time.

But to return to Christmas. One Christmas day I left my family at one o'clock in the morning. Christmas salutations were exchanged at that very sleepy hour and I took the fast express to a certain station whence I could drive up country to a little church in a farming country in which there had never been a Christmas service. It was a bitter cold morning, deep snow on the ground, and a furious north wind raging.

The climate is variable indeed out West. I have spent Christmas days on which it rained all day and of all days in the year on which to have it rain, Christmas is the worst. Still, the farmers would be thankful. It was usually safe to be thankful out there whenever it rained. I knew a man once who said you could make a fortune by always betting two to one that it would not rain, no matter what the present promise of the weather was. You were bound to win nine times out of ten.

I hired a good sleigh and two horses, and drove to my destination. The church was a little old brick building right out in the prairie. There was a smouldering fire in a miserable, worn-out stove which hardly raised the temperature of the room a degree although it filled the place with smoke. The wind had free entrance through the ill-fitting window and door frames and a little pile of snow formed on the altar during the service. I think there were twelve people who had braved the fury of the storm. There was not an evergreen within a hundred miles of the place and the only decoration was sagebrush. To wear vestments was impossible, and I conducted the service in a buffalo overcoat and a fur cap and gloves as I have often done. It was short and the sermon was shorter. Mem.: If you want short sermons give your Rector a cold church or a hot one!

After service I went to dinner at the nearest farm-house. Such a Christmas dinner it was! There was no turkey, and they did not even have a chicken. The menu was cornbread, ham, and potatoes, and mighty few potatoes at that. There were two children in the family, a girl of six and a boy of five. They were glad enough to get the ham. Their usual bill of fare was composed of potatoes and corn-bread, and sometimes corn-bread alone. My wife had put up a lunch for me, fearing that I might not be able to get anything to eat, in which there was a small mince-pie turnover; and the children had slipped a small box of candy in my bag as a Christmas gift. I produced the turnover which by common consent was divided between the astonished children. Such a glistening of eyes and smacking of small lips you never saw!

"This pie makes it seem like Christmas, after all," said the little girl, with her mouth full.

"Yes," said the boy, ditto, "that and the ham."

"We didn't have any Christmas this year," continued the small maiden. "Last year mother made us some potato men" (*i. e.*, little animal and semi-human figures made out of potatoes and matches with buttons

Christmas in the Snows 155

for eyes; they went into many stockings among the very poor out West then).

"But this year," interrupted the boy, "potatoes are so scarce that we couldn't have 'em. Mother says that next year perhaps we will have some real Christmas."

They were so brave about it that my heart went out to them. Children and no Christmas gifts! Only the chill, bare room, the wretched, meagre meal. I ransacked my brain. Finally something occurred to me. After dinner I excused myself and hurried back to the church. There were two small wicker baskets there which were used for the collection—old but rather pretty. I selected the best one. Fortunately I had in my grip a neat little "housewife" which contained a pair of scissors, a huge thimble, needles, thread, a tiny little pin-cushion, an emery bag, buttons, etc. I am, like most ex-sailors, something of a needleman myself. I emptied the contents into the collection basket and garnished the dull little affair with the bright ribbon ties ripped off the "housewife" and went back to the house.

To the boy I gave my penknife which happened to be nearly new, and to the girl the church basket with the sewing things for a work-basket. The joy of those children was one of the finest things I have ever witnessed. The face of the little girl was positively filled with awe as she lifted from the basket, one by one, the pretty and useful articles the "housewife" had supplied and when I added the small box of candy that my children had provided me, they looked at me with feelings of reverence, as a visible incarnation of Santa Claus. They were the cheapest and most effective Christmas presents it was ever my pleasure to bestow. I hope to be forgiven for putting the church furniture to such a secular use.

Another Christmas day I had a funeral. There was no snow, no rain. The day was warm. The woman who died had been the wife of one of the largest farmers in the diocese. He actually owned a continuous body of several thousands of acres of fine land, much of it under cultivation. She had been a fruitful mother and five stalwart sons, all married, and several daughters likewise, with numerous grandchildren represented her contribution to the world's population. They were the people of the most consideration in the little community in which they lived. We had the services in the morning in the Methodist church, which was big enough to hold about six hundred people. As it was a holiday, it was filled to the very doors. One of my farmer friends remarked as we stood on the front steps watching the crowd assembling:

"My, doc, all of them wagons gatherin'

here makes it seem more like circus day than a funeral."

I had been asked to preach a sermon, which I essayed to do. The confusion was terrific. In order to be present themselves the mothers in Israel had been obliged to bring their children, and the most domestic of attentions were being bestowed upon them freely. They cried and wailed and expostulated with their parents in audible tones until I was nearly frantic. I found myself shouting consoling platitudes to a sobbing, grief-stricken band of relatives and endeavouring to drown the noise of the children by roaring—the lion's part à la Bottom. It was distracting. I was a very young minister at the time and the perspiration fairly rained from me. That's what makes me remember it was a warm day.

When we got through the services after every one of the six hundred had, in the language of the local undertaker, "viewed the remains," we went to the cemetery. I rode behind a horse which was thirty-eight years old. I do not know what his original colour had been but at present he was white and hoary with age.

"I always use him for funerals," said the undertaker, "because he naturally sets the proper pace for a funeral procession."

"Mercy," said I, "I hope he won't die on the road."

"Well, if he does," continued the undertaker, "your services will come in handy. We can bury him proper. I am awful fond of that horse. I shouldn't wonder if he hadn't been at as many as a thousand funerals in his life."

I thought that he had all the gravity of his grewsome experiences, especially in his gait. The Christmas dinners were all late on account of the funeral but they were bountiful and good nevertheless and I much enjoyed mine.

Another Christmas I was snow-bound on one of the obscure branches of a Western railroad. If the train had been on time I would have made a connection and have reached home by Christmas Eve, but it was very evident, as the day wore on, that it was not going to be on time. Indeed it was problematical whether it would get anywhere at all. It was snowing hard outside. Our progress had become slower and slower. Finally in a deep cut we stopped. There were four men, one woman, and two little children in the car—no other passengers in the train. The train was of that variety known out West as a "plug" consisting of a combination baggage and smoker and one coach.

One of the trainmen started on a lonely and somewhat dangerous tramp of several miles up the road to the next station to call for the snow-plough, and the rest of us settled down to spend the night. Certainly we could not hope to be extricated before the next evening, especially as the storm then gave no signs of abating. We all went up to the front of the car and sat around the stove in which we kept up a bright fire,—fortunately we had plenty of fuel—and in such circumstances we speedily got acquainted with each other. One of the men was a "drummer," a travelling man for a notion house; another was a cow-boy; the third was a big cattle-man; and I was the last. We soon found that the woman was a widow who had maintained herself and the children precariously since the death of her husband by sewing and other feminine odd jobs but had at last given up the unequal struggle and was going back to live with her mother, also a widow who had some little property.

The poor little threadbare children had cherished anticipations of a joyous Christmas with their grandmother. From their talk we could hear that a Christmas tree had been promised them and all sorts of things. They were intensely disappointed at the blockade. They cried and sobbed and would not be comforted. Fortunately the woman had a great basket filled with substantial provisions which, by the way, she generously shared with the rest of us, so we were none of us hungry. As the night fell, we tipped up two of the seats, placed the bottoms sideways, and with our overcoats made two good beds for the little folks. Just before they went to sleep the drummer said to me:

"Say, parson, we've got to give those children some Christmas."

"That's what," said the cow-boy.

"I'm agreed," added the cattle-man.

"Madam," said the drummer, addressing

Christmas in the Snows

the woman with the easy assurance of his class, after a brief consultation between us, "we are going to give your kids some Christmas."

The woman beamed at him gratefully.

"Yes, children," said the now enthused drummer, as he turned to the open-mouthed children, "Santa Claus is coming round to-night sure. We want you to hang up your stockings."

"We ain't got none," quivered the little girl, "'ceptin' those we've got on and ma says it's too cold to take 'em off."

"I've got two new pair of woollen socks," said the cattle-man eagerly, "which I ain't never wore, and you are welcome to 'em."

There was a clapping of little hands in childish glee, and then the two faces fell as the elder remarked.

"But Santa Claus will know they are not

our stockings and he will fill them with things for you instead."

"Lord love you," said the burly cattle-man, roaring with infectious laughter, "he wont bring me nothin'. One of us will sit up anyway and tell him it's for you. You've got to hustle to bed right away because he may be here any time now."

Then came one of those spectacles which we sometimes meet once or twice in a lifetime. The children knelt down on the rough floor of the car beside their improvised beds. Instinctively the hands of the men went to their heads and at the first words of "Now I lay me down to sleep," four hats came off. The cow-boy stood twirling his hat and looking at the little kneeling figures; the cattle-man's vision seemed dimmed; while in the eyes of the travelling man there shone a distant look—a look across snow-filled prairies to a warmly lighted home.

The children were soon asleep. Then the rest of us engaged in earnest conversation. What should we give them? was the question.

"It don't seem to me that I've got anything to give 'em," said the cow-boy mournfully, "unless the little kid might like my spurs, an' I would give my gun to the little girl, though on general principles I don't like to give up a gun. You never know when you're goin' to need it, 'specially with strangers," he added with a rather suspicious glance at me. I would not have harmed him for the world.

"I'm in much the same fix," said the cattleman. "I've got a flask of prime old whiskey here, but it don't seem like it's very appropriate for the occasion, though it's at the service of any of you gents."

"Never seen no occasion in which whiskey wasn't appropriate," said the cow-boy, mellowing at the sight of the flask.

"I mean 'taint fit for kids," explained the cattle-man handing it over.

"I begun on't rather early," remarked the puncher, taking a long drink, "an' I always use it when my feelin's is onsettled, like now." He handed it back with a sigh.

"Never mind, boys," said the drummer. "You all come along with me to the baggage car."

So off we trooped. He opened his trunks, and spread before us such a glittering array of trash and trinkets as almost took away our breath.

"There," he said, "look at that. We'll just pick out the best things from the lot, and I'll donate them all."

"No, you don't," said the cow-boy. "My ante's in on this game, an' I'm goin' to buy what chips I want, an' pay fer 'em too, else there ain't going to be no Christmas around here."

"That's my judgment, too," said the cattleman.

"I think that will be fair," said I. "The travelling man can donate what he pleases, and we can each of us buy what we please, as well."

I think we spent hours looking over the stock which the obliging man spread out all over the car for us. He was going home, he said, and everything was at our service. The trainmen caught the infection, too, and all hands finally went back to the coach with such a load of stuff as you never saw before. We filled the socks and two seats besides with it. The grateful mother was simply dazed.

As we all stood about, gleefully surveying our handiwork including the bulging socks, the engineer remarked:

"We've got to get some kind of a Christmas tree."

So two of us ploughed off on the prairie—it

had stopped snowing and was bright moonlight—and wandered around until we found a good-sized piece of sage-brush, which we brought back and solemnly installed and the woman decorated it with bunches of tissue paper from the notion stock and clean waste from the engine. We hung the train lanterns around it.

We were so excited that we actually could not sleep. The contagion of the season was strong upon us, and I know not which were the more delighted the next morning, the children or the amateur Santa Clauses, when they saw what the cow-boy called the "layout."

Great goodness! Those children never did have, and probably never will have, such a Christmas again. And to see the thin face of that mother flush with unusual colour when we handed her one of those monstrous red plush albums which we had purchased

Christmas in the Snows

jointly and in which we had all written our names in lieu of our photographs, and between the leaves of which the cattle-man had generously slipped a hundred dollar bill, was worth being blockaded for a dozen Christmases. Her eyes filled with tears and she fairly sobbed before us.

During the morning we had a little service in the car, in accordance with the custom of the Church, and I am sure no more heartfelt body of worshippers ever poured forth their thanks for the Incarnation than those men, that woman, and the little children. The woman sang "Jesus Lover of my Soul" from memory in her poor little voice and that small but reverent congregation—cow-boy, drummer, cattle-man, trainmen, and parson—solemnly joined in.

"It feels just like church," said the cow-boy gravely to the cattle-man. "Say I'm all broke up; let's go in the other car and try your flask ag'in." It was his unfailing resource for "onsettled feelin's."

The train-hand who had gone on to division headquarters returned with the snow-plough early in the afternoon, but what was more to the purpose he brought a whole cooked turkey with him, so the children had turkey, a Christmas tree, and Santa Claus to their heart's content! I did not get home until the day after Christmas.

But, after all, what a Christmas I had enjoyed!

During a season of great privation we were much assisted by barrels of clothing which were sent to us from the East. One day just before Christmas, I was distributing the contents of several barrels of wearing apparel and other necessities to the women and children at a little mission. The delight of the women, as the good warm articles of clothing for themselves and their children which they so sadly needed were handed out to them was touching; but the children themselves did not enter into the joy of the occasion with the same spontaneity. Finally just as I got to the bottom of one box and before I had opened the other one, a little boy sniffling to himself in the corner remarked, *sotto voce:*

"Ain't there no real Chris'mus gif's in there for us little fellers, too?"

I could quite enter into his feelings, for I could remember in my youthful days when careful relatives had provided me with a "cardigan" jacket, three handkerchiefs, and a half-dozen pairs of socks for Christmas, that the season seemed to me like a hollow mockery and the attempt to palm off necessities as Christmas gifts filled my childish heart with disapproval. I am older now and can face a Christmas remembrance of a cookbook, a silver cake-basket, or an ice-cream freezer (some of which I have actually received) with philosophical equanimity, if not gratitude.

I opened the second box, therefore, with a great longing, though but little hope. Heaven bless the woman who had packed that box, for, in addition to the usual necessary articles, there were dolls, knives, books, games galore, so the small fry had some "real Chris'mus gif's" as well as the others.

After one of the blizzards a young ranchman who had gone into the nearest town some twenty miles away to get some Christmas things for his wife and little ones, was found frozen to death on Christmas morning, his poor little packages of petty Christmas gifts tightly clasped in his cold hands lying by his side. His horse was frozen too and when they found it, hanging to the horn of the saddle was a little piece of an evergreen tree —you would throw it away in contempt in the East, it was so puny. There it meant something. The love of Christmas? It was there in his dead hands. The spirit of Christmas? It showed itself in that bit of verdant pine over the lariat at the saddle-bow of the poor bronco.

Do they have Christmas out West? Well, they have it in their hearts if no place else, and, after all, that is the place above all others where it should be.

A Christmas Wish

A CHRISTMAS WISH

For Everybody, Everywhere

MAY peace and goodwill, prosperity and plenty, joy and satisfaction abound in your homes and in your hearts this day and all days. May opportunities for good work be many, and may you avail yourselves of them all. May your sorrows be lightened, may your griefs be assuaged. May your souls be fitted for what they must endure; may your backs be strengthened for your burdens; may your responsibilities be met; may your obligations be discharged; may your duties be performed. May love abound more and more until the perfect day breaks in your lives. In short, every wish that would be helpful, uplifting, and comforting, I wish you at this hour and in all hours.

In the words of Tiny Tim.

"God Bless us every one!"

CYRUS TOWNSEND BRADY.

*A Selection from the
Catalogue of*

G. P. PUTNAM'S SONS

**Complete Catalogue sent
on application**

And Thus He Came

By

Cyrus Townsend Brady

12°. Illustrated in Color. $1.00

A Christmas fantasy in which Jesus becomes a determining influence in the crises of human lives. The reader is given glimpses of touching little pictures ranging from the lighted ballrooms of society to the hopeless poverty of the slums, and of the need which in their several ways the children of men have for aid and solace from the Saviour of mankind.

G. P. Putnam's Sons

New York London

The More Excellent Way

By
Cyrus Townsend Brady

12°. *Color Frontispiece. $1.50 net. By mail, $1.60*

A tale of modern society and the divorce question, with the scenes laid in New York, Sorrento, Bermuda, and Reno. Rarely has an author, without attempt at preaching, written a story so subtly influential, so provocative of thought, even while it seems to leave no time for thought in the swift succession of its dramatic developments.

"'The More Excellent Way' deserves good place on the shelf of readable books."—*N. Y. Times.*

G. P. Putnam's Sons
New York   London

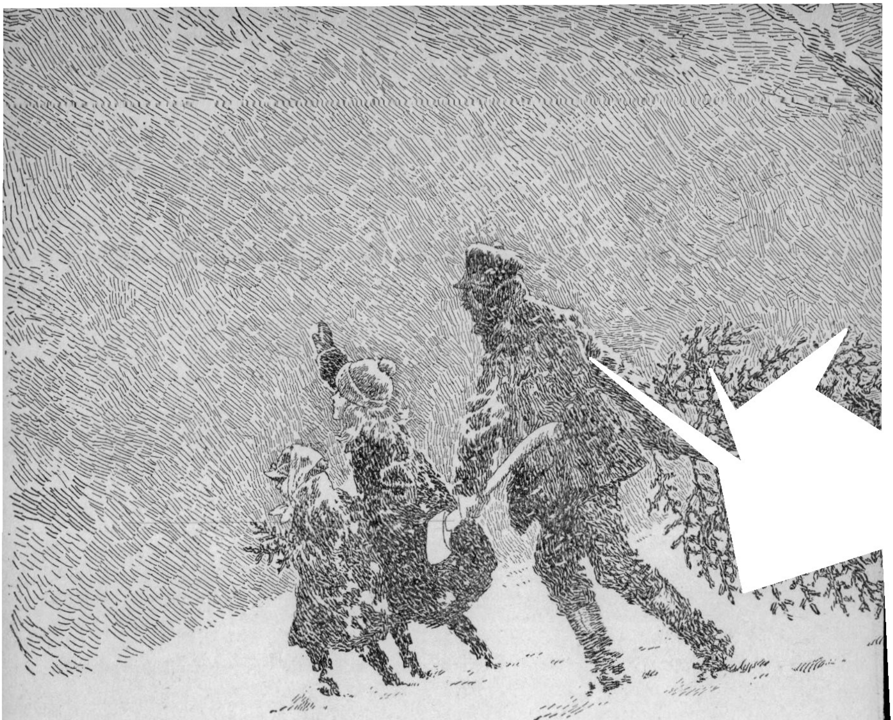

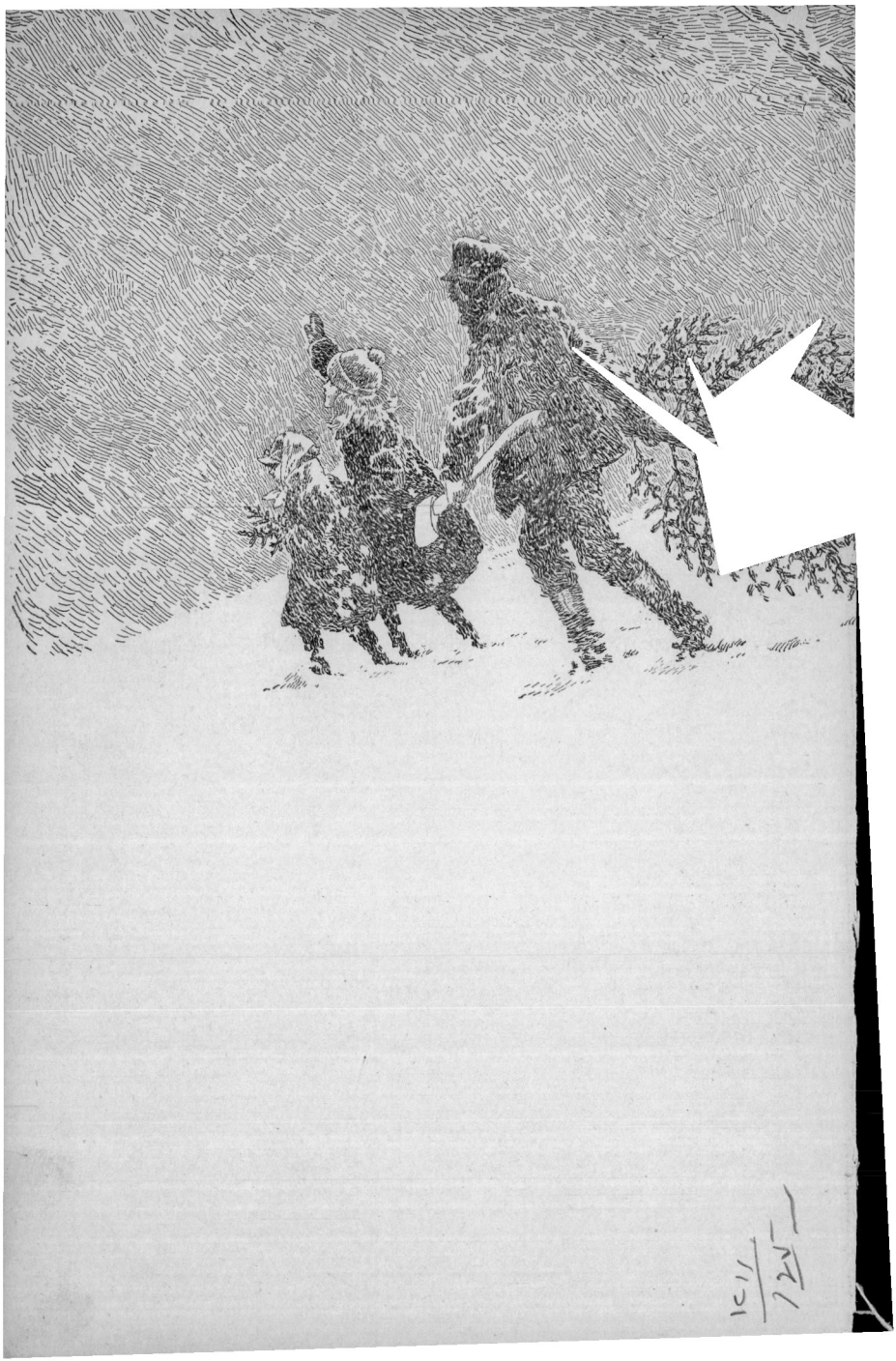